In The Service of Gaia:
The Call

George Drake, Ph.C.

Published by:
Common Sense For The Third Millennium
P.O. Box 7987
South Lake Tahoe, CA 96158, U.S.A.

ISBN-13: 978-0-9788246-1-7
ISBN-10: 0-9788246-1-X

Table of Contents

Foreword

A great deal has transpired since first I penned *The Call*, most of it negative. But none came even close to the increase in the human population by about 350 million, or 5%. That occurred in only five years.

Since the initial event of this book took place, the world's population has increased by approximately 2.5 billion or, essentially, half again what it was in 1986.

Some developments, small as they were, however, have served well to validate this work, including its selection for reading and discussion in a theological seminar taught by Prof. Christopher Southgate at Exeter University in England, the reluctant e-mail confirmation of the possibility of its most dire prediction by Anne Ehrlich, the wife and Stanford University colleague of Paul Ehrlich, author of *The Population Bomb*, and, most profoundly, the spontaneous bursting into tears on a crowded airplane by a young man named Jeremy, who actually got what I am trying to say.

I'm writing a new book which will contain an updated version of the following, and much more, but I needed additional copies of the original to give away, for time is of the essence. If you purchased this book, and aren't moved to support my ongoing efforts to get its message out by helping me cover its costs, e-mail me at gwdrake@intheserviceofgaia.com and I will refund that portion of your money which came to me as a consequence of your expense. If you want to do more, just e-mail me with "volunteer" in the subject line.

But please, because I am not in this for profit, but do wish, urgently, to communicate to as many as I can, give this book to someone else.

Thank you.

Chapter 1
Introduction

Beziers

Although my story really began in 1986, this book started much later. My wife, Barbara, and I were on European holiday in the summer of 2001. The little city of Beziers has a wonderful cathedral which you can see as you approach by auto from the south. We wanted a picture, but there's nowhere to pull over until the bottom of a little grade, and from there the view is obstructed by the rail right-of-way.

As we pulled off the road, a passenger train sped by, going about as fast as I'd ever seen a train travel. I know trains. I put myself through college by working first as a freight brakeman and then as a switchman for the Southern Pacific Railroad. My father was a train dispatcher. As a boy, I used to walk about four miles along the main line to go fishing nearly every day of every summer. So I know trains. I'm extremely comfortable around them. American trains, at least. Not hesitating, I scrambled up onto this French track, observed that one could see quite far in both directions, and confidently began taking pictures, conscientiously checking both ways at frequent intervals.

In the western U.S., the passing of a passenger train is a virtual guarantee of a long spell without another. I knew enough not to expect the same thing in Europe, but I was surprised, nonetheless, when, as I was focusing for only the third shot, a train whistle sounded–quite close. Startled, I automatically stepped backward. Unfortunately, this put me directly in front of the train, which was only about 250 yards away and moving so fast that the engine rocked vigorously from side to side. I had never seen an engine bouncing back and forth so energetically before and found myself transfixed, watching its jerky dance as it bore down on me. I could imagine men inside hanging onto their chairs as the cab shook violently. I thought, "What a rough ride French engine crews must have."

I'm not sure how long it was before I "came to," for I had no sense of time, but as soon as I'd observed the plight of the badly shaken crew, my brain began issuing some rather stern instructions, "Don't look at the train, George! Get off the track!" Momentarily, I contemplated which way to jump. An image crossed my mind of a squirrel dashing across the highway in front of my car, then inexplicably reversing course only to be squashed. Best not to think about it. I kept going in the direction I'd started.

The engineer was now frantically blasting his horn, and I could easily judge the train's distance without looking. It was less than 100 yards away. I took one step and began the running forward roll I'd learned decades earlier as a judoka at San Jose State College. The horn continued resounding. It was almost on me.

As my right foot propelled me into the air, I looked at the rail and involuntarily visualized my body severed at the waist–a not uncommon way for switchmen to die when I worked for the railroad. When a man is caught against the rail by a train's wheels the effect is exactly like a pair of giant scissors slicing him in half. The internal command warned, "Clear the rail!" and I exaggerated the arch of my body so I wouldn't get hung up. The horn was not more than thirty feet away.

And that puts the cowcatcher much closer still.

While every thought until then is indelibly etched in my memory, I have no recollection of landing on the same sharp volcanic cinder rock we use for roadbed in the U.S., nor do I recall the head tuck and shoulder roll

1-2

which I know from my judo experience must have followed. I do remember the sound of the train roaring by at a speed well in excess of a hundred miles an hour, only three feet from my head. I lay motionless on the ballast until the train passed, which took only a second or two despite a length of about fifteen cars. As soon as it was gone, I was on my feet, absolutely ecstatic, and not even so much as bruised, scratched, or scraped. Apparently, it had been one of the best forward rolls of my life.

No, it was *absolutely* the best forward roll of my life!

I was elated. I was alive! Watching the train rolling away like the back end of a falling star, all I could think was, "I'm alive! It missed me! Yes, yes, yes!"

Half running, I scrambled down the embankment and began to make my way back to the car. Suddenly the adrenaline shock struck, and my knees began to tremble. As I began to cross the road, I was afraid my legs might buckle. Barbara sat in the car awaiting my return, reading her novel. She clearly suspected nothing amiss. My strength completely gone, my heart pounding, my breath shallow and rapid, and my elbows now a match for my knees, I crossed to her side of the car and said through the open window "you've got to drive."

Looking up, she instantly realized something was definitely wrong. She asked, "What happened? Are you alright?"

"Yeah, I'm fine. But you've got to drive."

"Lover, what happened?"

"A train almost hit me, but I'm fine. You've got to drive."

She got out to change seats and I was barely able to collapse into her place before I almost couldn't move from the aftereffects of the adrenaline. As she drove I told her of my near miss through tears of relief and remorse for fifteen fallow years, while my mind retraced every instant of the last five minutes over and over again in minute detail, all the while with one theme blaring through my consciousness like that screaming train: *"What are you going to tell Mother? If you die and haven't done a **damn** thing about the Vision, what are you going to say? How will you admit such a failure to **her**?? Huh? How?"*

Buddha's Song

Fifteen years earlier, alone in another part of Europe, I had a Vision–like in the Bible. And yes, I know how that sounds. But it was no vague impression, not a flash of insight. It was so devastating, so galling, that I'd spent most of the intervening years denying its imperative and stifling all self-exhortation to take it public. I told no one but a very few close friends hoping, mainly, for reassurance that I wasn't absolutely insane. Someone as anti-religious as I just isn't supposed to see "Visions."

Instead of fully accepting the prophecy and its preposterous Message, I made conciliatory efforts to meet its commands in reasonable, acceptable ways. Almost surreptitiously, I also gathered evidence relevant to the premonition, desperately hoping that I could prove to myself that, really, I was just crazy. Better deranged than accept that horrific view of the future as true.

For I'd been shown the end of life on the Earth, and all I really wanted was to repudiate the knowledge, pretend it had never happened, and forget about it altogether. I certainly didn't want to think about it or talk about it, much less proclaim it from a soapbox.

Repress it as I might, however, that unwelcome Vision was never far from my thoughts. That day in Beziers I'd been shown another light: I didn't have forever. I would die someday and when and how was entirely out of my control. If I didn't move on the Vision, *now*, then I'd die in the middle of trying to get up my nerve. In the final analysis and despite all these disclaimers, that's what I'd been trying to do ever since having had it.

How to do it, though? That was the problem. How do I share something so extraordinary it defies normal means of communication?

Let's start with something which might seem unrelated, but isn't.

*[Here I want you to prepare for listening to the C.D. included with this book. You'll need a Compact Disc player, or a computer, or go to http://www.intheserviceofgaia.com and download one of the Trumpeting files to your iPod ®. Hopefully, this recording may pull you out of the day-to-day reality you were experiencing when you picked this book up a few minutes ago. **Before you play it, though,** let me tell you what you'll be hearing: as with most things in life, there's an extensive, and important, context.]*

One day, while struggling with what it meant that I should be a witness to a Vision and how to cope with it, I had another, equally extreme, experience. I was on one of my sojourns to my favorite beach. This particular beach is one of the most wonderful remaining examples of how the Earth was before man learned agriculture. The sky is always cobalt blue, unless it is cloudy, which it often is. This beach is incredibly beautiful, large and nearly undiscovered. Many are the times I've spent an entire day on it without seeing a single human being. Oddly, but entirely compatible with the ambiance of the place, there's also almost never any high altitude air traffic–which is ubiquitous almost everywhere else.

I am always moved by the abundance of nature there. Where man's impact is minimal, plants and animals of all sorts flourish. I was feeling the mixed emotions evoked by the contrast between the cornucopia of life we still have on Earth today and the immensity of the loss I had foreseen.

The freedom of being totally alone allowed me grieve over the Vision, then only two years old. I was sobbing openly. Attempting to regain my composure, I decided to meditate by repeating the "om" sound. But as I began, I was literally startled by the sound that I actually produced, for it was unlike any I had ever made before, or heard anyone else make. It had started as "om" all right, but had suddenly morphed into something quite different.

[Please begin playing the C.D. now, as I continue the sound's story.]

Perhaps it was because I was so choked up, I can't say, but for whatever reason, the sound went from "om" to an unvoiced, almost musical, intonation which was more–much more–like the sound of a trumpet than a chant. It was very like a French horn. Not even that, precisely, but beautiful and quite loud. I could hold the note for a surprisingly long time, as I was using very little air in producing it. But the oddest thing about the sound was that I wasn't sure how I was making it.

I attempted, successfully, to do it again. And again. It was fascinating. Beautiful and totally effortless. It was the most relaxing sound–*experience*, even–that I have ever known. I spent that entire day doing absolutely nothing but Trumpeting (for that was the obvious name to describe it, since "French Horning" grates on the ear). But no amount of physical self-evaluation clarified how I was managing to make the noise at all. It was very much like whistling in that the air apparently vibrated in passing through an opening of a certain shape. But the aperture was not formed by the lips. It was further back, probably in the esophagus or even lower. Because of the depth of the tone produced and the fact that it commenced as a voiced "om" sound, I couldn't dislodge the impression that the vocal cords were involved. Yet any conscious engagement of the larynx instantly changed its nature into something very much more mundane. Its volume was simply extraordinary. With practice, this aspect only increased.

[Listen closely to see if you can hear the overtones that began enriching the sound as that beautiful day wore on and my soft palate apparently grew warmer. Some notes are as high as a whistle and others very low in tone. These high and low notes are being produced simultaneously. The overlay of two tracks, which is how the C.D. was made, may obscure that fact. I think the combination of tracks, however, is worth the confusion because it enhances the meditative aspects of the sound. As you read on, you'll learn that this reproduction is not perfect, being a recovered gift. I'm telling the story here of how I lost and regained the sound to satisfy your curiosity regarding the inclusion of such an odd C.D. and to expose you early on to exactly how unusual my tale will prove to be.]

I found myself in deep meditation, something I had never achieved before. My thinking process, though, was not so much halted as freed from it's usual restraint of logical deduction, instilled through years of teaching mathematics. Contemplating its volume, I fantasized this sound as the one that Joshua and his band of soldiers used in their assault on Jericho. Instead of using actual horns, perhaps they just Trumpeted. I imagined metal hinges in stone resonating with the vibration and working themselves loose from their moorings, collapsing the doors in a heap to be run through at will. If there were a multitude making it, the sound would be as deafening as it was beautiful. The besieged would feel as if God produced it Himself.

For so it seemed to me.

I was not making the sound at all, I fancied. I was only breathing. The Lifeforce itself was flowing through me. I was an instrument, nothing more nor less.

It was *truly* magical.

Similar thoughts came to me throughout the day. What a splendor, this sound! I imagined using it to confront the numerous examples of stupidity, or dishonesty, that I frequently encountered in professional meetings where idiotic or even evil programs were sanguinely discussed and clever plans laid. I'd simply Trumpet over the B.S. I have no doubt whatsoever that such a tactic would stop bullshit dead in its tracks. The sound was irresistible. It's logic and beneficence undeniable and compelling.

Eventually, the sound began pulsing in volume exactly as happens when tuning a piano with a tuning fork.

[I regret that neither the incredibly high decibel level, nor this harmonic resonance, is duplicated on the C.D. [1]]

When evening began to fall, I walked back to the car, Trumpeting much of the way. As I approached the trailhead, I spied a small herd of bull elk grazing between me and my van. I approached quietly and then, from about fifteen yards, began Trumpeting. Long habituated to humans, the elk usually ignore us completely. But they had obviously never heard one of us Trumpet before. Every animal instantly raised his head, stopped the incessant chewing of his cud and stared. Ten racks held high in silent salute. And so they remained, motionless, as I Trumpeted to them for about ten minutes. I felt as one with the universe.

I continued on to the car, the only vehicle at the parking spot, and was surprised to see a couple approaching on foot. Like the elk, they seemed to regard me as quite peculiar. I realized they had also been listening, and were equally astonished. They barely acknowledged me, but I could see how very curious they were, apparently wondering what instrument I had and where it had disappeared to, or perhaps just how strange I was.

On the drive home, I stopped to visit friends in Placerville. Over dinner, I told them of my extraordinary experience and the magical sound I had been making all that day. They wanted to hear, so I

---

[1]For a demonstration of some more recent performances (it just seems to keep getting closer and closer to the original) go to http://www.intheserviceofgaia.com

demonstrated. Their one-year-old son immediately stopped eating and gazed at me from his highchair in rapt attention. Neither of his parents, though, seemed much impressed. Linda said "That sounds like the chanting the Tibetan Buddhist monks do." (To this day, after numerous exposures to such chanting, I still think this assessment misses Trumpeting's extraordinariness.) Dave's response was equally dismissive.

I was crestfallen that they had not instantly recognized Trumpeting as a tool with tremendous potential. Recalling the curious stares, I was simultaneously crushed and embarrassed. The next morning, when finally alone in my car, I attempted Trumpeting again. But I could not make the sound. Try as I might, it proved itself ephemeral. Everything I tried came out strained, off pitch, non-reverberative and completely lacking in volume. My efforts all originated somewhere in the vocal cords instead of springing spontaneously from the flow of the air. I apparently was no longer relaxed enough to trumpet, or perhaps I was simply trying too hard to imitate something I had heard somewhere.

My magical ability to Trumpet had vanished.

I tried unsuccessfully to re-create the sound for some fifteen years, but usually only when alone. Until 2003 I made no progress at all. By 2004, I was beginning to make headway on my other goal, retiring from teaching to pursue my Mission. Not coincidentally, I think, my performances improved. At first, I was only able to Trumpet in the shower, where the resonance from the tile helped. After so many years, it was very encouraging. I think it shows how enchanting the original sound had been that, after only one day of "having it" I was compelled to pursue it fruitlessly for fifteen years.

The closest thing to the original sound I've heard since losing it is not the chanting, but the horns used by Tibetan monks: the ones which are about 12 feet long and require three people to play–two to hold the instrument and one to blow into it. The horns are played in the coronation scene from the movie, *The Man Who Would Be King,*[2] and they are almost identical to Trumpeting in both volume and tone, save for the high overtones, which they don't seem to share. There are numerous similar sounds, from the throat singing of the Dhuva, an obscure tribe from somewhere near Afghanistan, to the Australian Aboriginal's didgeridoo, the Arabic call to prayers, and even some American Indian singing. Might this sound, in some ancient incarnation, be the origin of many of the various meditation devices used by religions around the world–the original "om?"

[I believe the meditation induced by listening to the C.D. may serve as a powerful asset as you read further. So please establish the habit of playing Trumpeting in the background. Namaste.]

---

[2]*The Man Who Would Be King,* directed by John Huston, Columbia Pictures, 1975

Chapter 2
Stranger Than Fiction,
More Horrible Than Fact

George Drake:
At Least Nominally Normal
I shall begin my full story by exposing you to
who I am, for you may well be dubious: you know me
not at all and likely your only previous experience with
people who lay claim to Visions is some poor nut-case
who begged you to give him/her a quarter on the street.
You deserve some reasons not to dismiss me out of
hand.
For one thing, I'm not a religious freak. I admit,
however, that my pursuit of the rational haven of
mathematics, which I spent a career teaching at the
college level, may well have been an overreaction to the
rabidly devout fundamentalist faith of my Southern
Baptist parents. My mom was the most domineering
person I've ever met, and definitely a prime example of
the kind of person who, in the 1980's and beyond, would
become the backbone of the "Christian Right."
For a while, at least, she took the whole family
with her. Had you known her, that would not be
particularly surprising. God was her one and only judge.
The woman adhered to the Word and the Word
commanded true believers to take action for right and
justice, whether or not it was popular with their peers–or
their family. For example, Mother once got an
extremely popular new high school football coach fired
for condoning hazing. This was no easy task in small-
town America of the fifties, especially with this coach
who, in his first year, had turned the team's longstanding
losing history around one hundred-and-eighty degrees.

It was natural that I spent my pre-teen, teen, and young adult years as a devout Southern Baptist. Following Billy Graham's relentless badgering for money after I'd "rededicated my life to Jesus" during Billy's San Francisco revival in 1956, however, my relationship to churches began to change. The Right Reverend Billy Graham was much more interested in my money than my soul, and that realization affected how I've seen religion every since.

Even having seen a Vision myself has not dislodged the deep disdain and skepticism with which I eventually came to regard virtually all organized religions. They may talk a good game, but most are far too concerned with money and power to have meaningful insight into the spiritual realm. Unfortunately, the truth of this observation is in direct proportion to the square of the height of the organization's, or its current leader's, public profile.

The straw that finally completely broke the back of my youthful addiction to religion was the discovery in the Sixties of the joy that came with truly inspired sex. In one absolutely fantastic encounter with a creative and entirely uninhibited lover, I realized that the Baptist preoccupation with guilt and hatred was focused in exactly the wrong place. Love, in any of its many forms, is far better than hate in any of its, far more numerous, disguises. They'd been lying to me all those years. Sex was not evil. I could see that for myself.

I've never looked back.

Despite my disenchantment with religion, however, I purposefully still adhere to my mother's strong sense of justice and moral imperative, living by the conviction that one must follow one's conscience, striving always to do the right thing–to take a stand–to take action. Her's was an example worth following.

Perhaps you can understand, then, my concern, triggered by that close encounter with a train, over having to explain to Mother–and even worse, to myself–why I'd done nothing about the Vision for fifteen years. It's not as if there were any ambiguity about what I was *supposed* to be doing with my life.

As a professional mathematician, I've always been dedicated to the rational mind, the provable, the demonstrable, the discernible. Mathematics is not a discipline which includes Visions of disaster or commands to "save the world." I am–or was–incredulous of Visions and Visionaries. I have no use for and no patience with mystical revelations, new-age fanatics, astrologers, religious charlatans or anything else which relies solely on the intuitive mind, parapsychology, pseudo-science, wishful thinking, misleading documentation or, as my wife (a reluctant spiritualist herself) wryly refers to it, any of that other "spiritual mumbo-jumbo." Or, at least, I didn't until it happened to me.

As a college professor, I was a damn good teacher: demanding, but with a good sense of humor. I was very well liked by my students, who were sometimes surprised by how much solid math they learned. I served on the Executive Committee of the Academic Senate for California Community Colleges. I've also succeeded in community leadership roles beyond the somewhat esoteric domain of academia. I served as president of South Lake Tahoe's Kiwanis Sunrisers club and once received their "Kiwanian of the Year" award, achieving both these honors several years after I had the Vision. A list of similar accomplishments is available on line.[3]

You'd never know by looking at or talking to me that I had seen a Vision with a capital "V." This thing has shaken my rational mind to its core and into my soul. It confounds and surprises me even today. It's rumbled discordantly through every activity, major decision, and relationship of my life for the past twenty years.

I assure you, I wasn't happy about it. I wasn't expecting it, didn't want it, wasn't seeking it and didn't welcome it. I certainly don't consider it any kind of gift.

The Vision (1): Prophecy

I took a sabbatical leave to England in the fall of 1986. I spent the preceding summer bicycling on my own through France, Holland, Germany, and Switzerland. It was my first trip to Europe and I was having a perfectly wonderful time, save for being lonely while away from my lover of then some three years. (We're married now and have been together twenty-three years–which I mention as additional evidence of my "stability.")

In the Netherlands everything changed. Those who know the Netherlands may well suspect that drugs played a part in my experience. But, I assure you, I was not under the influence of any mind-altering substance. It was no hallucination, and not a "flashback." Not dreamlike. Not even a surreal quality. I would have welcomed surreal.

---

[3]   If you're that interested, see my resume on the website at http://www.intheserviceofgaia.com

I was pedaling along quite placidly, as the roads there are all flat. Traffic was no issue. Holland is famous for its ubiquitous bicycle paths which make cycling there such a safe pleasure. If the number of hog farms is any indication, the Dutch are inordinately fond of pork, as the countryside is replete with these offensive "nose-sores." At that moment, though, there was no hint of the stench that can sometimes overwhelm an unsuspecting cyclist. Instead the air was clean and fresh, the sky a clear blue. It was a splendid summer day for cycling, and all was well with the world.

Then I glanced up at the little tree-covered hillside I was passing.

And the world died.

All the trees–every leaf, every blade of grass–were parched. Crinkled. Brown. Nothing moved. Nothing lived. *Nothing.* Down to the micro-organisms in the soil and the lichen on the stones. Everything on that little hill was dead, wizened and sere. *Every*thing.

I can't explain how I knew this, for you can't see everything on a hill by looking at it from a bicycle. But I knew. Knew with absolute certainty.

I saw the sky had turned a sickening yellowish-grey, toxic to all forms of life, palpable and impossible to breathe. There was no water–not a *trace* of moisture. Amid that unspeakably gruesome scene, it was perhaps the utter lack of water that struck me as most fundamental.

"What the . . .?" I thought. And the instantaneous answer seared into my being with unequivocal certainty: I had been transported to the future. The year I didn't know; But I did know the entire planet was as harshly arid and dead as that hill.

Then came a Message–and I *do* mean to capitalize the word, for it was not just some exceptional insight. I cannot actually say whether I heard a voice from outside myself or whether it was all internal. If the latter, it was not the voice I use when talking silently to myself, like when my brain would order me off the train track years later in Beziers. I wasn't *thinking*; I was being *addressed*.

"We're not going to make it."

That was the first part of a two-part message. Very simple, but conveying a complete, deep and surprisingly complex meaning. Although I emphasize the words in print via bold script, I cannot say it was particularly loud–just a solid, very clear statement of the harshest fact possible, like smashing without warning into a granite cliff or being caught in the open by a severe and abrupt hail storm. No shelter. No moderation.

The second part, however, bore the slightest glimmer of hope, and has now become my life's work, but I will share that second part later for fear that giving it away here will dilute the first. Strangely, while the first is the easiest to believe and the least alien to our current cultural milieu, it is, by far, the hardest for most people to understand–to truly *comprehend*. I must not allow anything to obscure the profound reality of this part of the Vision.

Life on Earth will not survive. The Lifeforce will die. It will do so soon–on the order of hundreds of years. *"We're **not** going to make it."*

Hole in the Wall

At this point, I must digress a bit because I recognize how my own history has repeated itself as I've related the Vision to you just now, and how I may be failing you by allowing that to happen. In my life, I've survived three near death experiences unscathed. The closest call, as you've heard, was in Beziers. The first time was years before, when I thought I might drown. It was surely the least serious of the three, but it taught me two important lessons.

I was at a little beach called "Hole in the Wall," so named because the sea had carved an arched passageway through a cliff between two small beaches. On this particular summer day in or around 1971, there was a storm just out to sea making the surf so high that one couldn't cross through the arch to the more private beach. It was hot and clear, but very windy. The accessible beach was thick with people, though the violent surf deterred most from swimming.

I had to pee, so, lacking a private place to go, I waded into the water just far enough to be able to urinate unnoticed. I was only about thigh deep, and hadn't yet begun my task, when a large wave swept me off my feet. Startled to be suddenly swimming, my attention shifted to the next wave, which I caught for a nice ride toward the shore. When I stood up, though, I could barely reach the ground and couldn't maintain contact as the relentless surf struck again. With the next wave, I got an even better ride, but this time couldn't touch bottom at all. Sculling my arms to keep head above water, I thought to myself, "That should have done it, it was a good wave. Try it one more time." Then my more cautious side asserted itself, speaking emphatically inside my head, "No, George, call for help *now*–while you're still not tired!"

Even back then I had a healthy respect for the part of myself that addresses me in that tone of voice. I called for help. Because the bottom dropped off so sharply from the shore, I was only about fifteen yards from the crowd on the sand. People could easily hear me. Several stood and looked out at me, puzzled, and a few even began to walk down closer to the water.

"Help!" I called again. From their expressions I could tell that they were thinking, "Is this guy serious?" I understood instantly why they wondered. Despite having yelled at the top of my voice, I didn't sound the least bit convincing. I had called out in a rather polite, "would you mind giving me a hand" kind of tone, as if I'd left my keys on the beach or something.

I was alarmed by the idea that they might not believe me. I could drown here! As if my lungs, diaphragm and larynx had made a snap decision on their own, I cried out again, but this time with no restraint in my voice *at all*. Now there was no mistaking it: I needed help. The sound of my own voice, so totally authentic in its plea for help, scared the hell out of me.

There was only one other swimmer in the water and he heard me this time and swam over, stopping about ten feet away. Treading water, he asked, "What's the matter?"

In what must have been an incredibly panicky voice, I replied, "I'm not panicked yet, but you've gotta help me. I can't get to shore."

He explained that I was in a rip tide but if we swam parallel to the shore we would get out of it and could then swim in. He moved closer, cautiously took me by the elbow, and calmly escorted me on the route that would get us out. In about twenty minutes, I was safely on shore again–but totally exhausted. I was very glad I'd not waited for one more wave, and especially so when Cole, my rescuer, told me that he'd intended to catch the next wave in himself and wouldn't have been in the water much longer. Cole was an off duty lifeguard and I've often ruminated on how lucky I was that day.

At the end of the drama, however, I still needed to pee–now desperately. Needless to say, this time I didn't let modesty stop my doing it on land in clear view of anyone who wanted to watch.

The Vision (1A):
Dead Planet Spinning
So here's how I'm failing you in relating the story of the Vision: there's no panic in my voice, and I again have great fear I won't be taken seriously in my call for help. Most people, never having seen the Earth entirely dead, will not grasp the horror of it. The loss. Oh, *my God*, the loss! *Every*thing on that hill was dead. *Every*thing on Earth will be dead.

Surveying that hillside was viscerally different from looking at photos of Mars. Mars is, and appears to have always been, Lifeless. Earth will die. This was death I saw, not the mere absence of Life. Look around you. You are surrounded by life. It is there in the spider in the corner, the houseplant in the window, the cockroaches in the pantry, the mold on the baseboard, the bacteria in your bowels. And they were *all* dead. Their bodies were there, littering the whole planet. They *will* all be dead. Yes, even the cockroaches.

Since that moment, there has never been a day pass in which I haven't *marveled* at how much life there is on this planet. Seeing it all deceased makes it impossible to take for granted. Living with the knowledge it will die has been an unimaginable curse; living with the newfound appreciation of today's vibrant land of plenty, a bittersweet blessing.

But to really hear the urgency in my cry, *you* need to try to imagine for yourself the loss. Go to a window and look out. If you're in a city you may not notice anything but humanity's impact at first. But look more closely: Trees, grass, birds, and the omnipresent insects: *all dead*. Every one. Fruit markets? Forget it. Fruit flies? History. And all those people? Dead. Every one. Every age. Every color. Love, hate, or merely tolerate them–dead.

Imagine the sky a pale yellowish haze, not very unlike the skies over most of our cities today, but worse. Impossible to breathe. Asphyxiating. Asphyxiating not just to us, or even only to primates. Poisonous to cats and dogs, to lice and elephants. Smothering snakes and snails, trees and lichen, microbes and fungi. Toxic to *everything*. Toxic, yet sparse. I had the very strong impression that the air was simply too thin to hold moisture.

There will be no water, for sure. No oxygen, most likely. No life. *No life at all.* More than anything else, what was evident in the Vision was this: we *will* lose the water from this planet. And so, the fish and shrimp and dolphins and gastropods die as well. Oh, we will have done with the mosquito. But small consolation for also losing clouds, fog, dew and rain.

Without water, everything dies. *Every*thing dies.

Nowhere on the surface of the Earth is life absent–not the coldest ice floes nor the hottest springs, nor even the deepest oceanic trenches–life flourishes everywhere on Earth.
It's all going to die.
I'm afraid I've been making this sound as if the whole thing is my personal experience–*my* problem–*my* story. But it's not some sort of diversion intended for idle reading on the subway. Not some story to lull you to sleep at night. It's not just my personal

experience–just my take on reality–*my* version of the environmental issue–an odd tale of a weird thing that happened to me one day on a bicycle. It's not even just *humanity's* story, for God's sake.

Every blade of grass on that hill was dead. *Every* insect, *every* flower. *Every* worm. *Every* mite. *Every* bacterium! And it was no mere image of what might happen if we don't get our act together. It was a view of what *will be* Of what *will* be true *every*where on Earth. It was not some kind of warning–a call to reform or repent, or to change our ways. It was nothing like that. It was prophecy, pure and simple. It *was* the future.

Everywhere on Earth will be lifeless. *Lifeless!* No bats, no bears, no crops, no weeds. No moss. No one-celled plants or animals. Someday–someday much sooner than any scientist has ever predicted for the end of Earth–the air will be too toxic to breathe. No form of life will survive.

And, the very worst of all, *nothing* we can do will prevent it.

The Rapture?
I Don't Think So!

If they don't dismiss me out of hand, most people hearing about my Vision immediately conclude that I witnessed God's wrath upon us, his wayward people. That is *so* not what this Vision was about. Quite the contrary, the Vision was extraordinarily clear on that point. The end of the Earth will not be about humans. *All* life on this teeming planet is doomed. But the universe does not suddenly end. The universe is not about Earth. And, harder for most people to accept, God is not particularly concerned about us humans.

I think it is this aspect of having seen the Vision which sets me farthest apart from those who have never had a similar experience. I am no longer human-centric in my thinking.

It is natural for most people to think in human-centric terms because it is an instinctual reaction of all living entities. We have no other choice: we *have* to consider *our* lives as being "about us." That is, essentially, what self-awareness is. And it applies to every living being there is. Every creature must have some sort of "life."

While it is clearly beyond my abilities to conceive of what an individual from another species experiences, still it seems safe to say that each creature's universe is identical with its life experience. We each have our own, personal universe, and yours *is* about you, just as mine is about me, and my dog, Sunny's, is about her. But it is absurd to make the jump from "my universe is about me" to "the universe is about humans." How did Sunny get left out there?

Thinking that *every*thing is about us humans is simply wrong. Yet this is a central tenet of all western religions, at least. Unfortunately I don't know enough to include eastern, but I see little in their practices to make me expect any differently of them.

The Message of the Vision, however, was about *Life*, not *humans*.

This was not a story about us being beamed up to some kind of Heaven, or down to some awful Hell. Humans were conspicuous by their absence, at least insofar as being *particularly* missed. We did not even register as an afterthought or an aside. It was about *so* much more. The most memorable thing about the Vision was the overwhelming emotional storm surge consisting entirely of the realization of what it *means* to say that "all life on Earth is going to perish."

In comparison, whether humans survive or not is an *absolutely* trivial matter. Humans are a mere twig in the haystack of Life. It's not *at all* about *us*. And if the universe is not *about us,* then Earth's end is not going to be about "the Rapture."

As I write this, I find myself crying, just as I did that day in Holland. As soon as I got the Message, tears burst forth–uncontrolled, uncontrollable. Deep, wracking sobs. Blurring my vision as I rode on down the once again perfectly normal path. The Vision had taken less than a few seconds, but I wept for what must have been another half mile before I lumbered to a stop, got off my overladen bike, and just sat there, in grief as I'd never known it. Grief so stark and deep that I've never been free of it since. I have no recollection of anything else that day. My memory ends, sitting on the ground, helmet at my feet, hunched over my knees with mucous and water of every sort dripping off my face and falling soundlessly to a firmament I'd never treasured so much before.

Crazy

Before continuing, I want to restate my previous disclaimer: Having had a Vision seems entirely atypical of who I am. I would have loved to have spent chapter upon chapter convincing you of how bizarre it is that this happened to me. Had I done so, you'd probably have already put this book down, for my story prior to this event is not particularly interesting. I don't understand what happened that day. I can't explain it, and it's taken me two decades to face up to the Mission that was set for me in the Vision's second part. Understand it or not, however, the full force of what I'm trying to tell you is compelling me forward, and I must address in more detail my concerns that people may think I'm crazy.

First of all, the means of the Earth's demise, as I foresaw it, seems absurd. The Earth would be far better named if it were called "The Oceans." Three-fourths of this planet is covered with water, much of it to depths of ten miles or more. By contrast, Mount Everest is measured only in feet. Earth is truly the home of water. Throughout the solar system, only Earth has true liquid aquatic oceans[4]. The amount of water on this planet is astounding. Yet *I* believe its just going to be gone one day?

That's crazy. Certainly so at first blush.

Toxic air? That's easy enough to imagine. You only have to visit Mexico City, Los Angeles, Hong Kong, or any major city in the world and look up at the sky. Looking down from above makes the point even better. There have even been plenty of historical examples of truly toxic air. The Killer Fog of London and the disasters of Bhopal and (in a slightly different way) Chernobyl, come easily to mind. Yet even these examples are, at most, regional in extent.

But . . . air too thin to hold water? How absurd. Earth's atmosphere is far deeper than the ocean. We live at the bottom of this Earth-enshrouding gas blanket and rarely even think about it. Oh, we marvel at its tendency to take on beautiful colors at sunrise and sunset. And we

---

[4]Europa, a moon of Jupiter, is covered in water, but it is a frozen ocean. There may be liquid water below the ice, however. Also, new information from Enceladus, one of Saturn's moons, may indicate another water spot in Sol's system,.

think about storms, of course, but rarely associate them with the simple fact that they are nothing more than eddies in this globe-encircling river of moving air and water vapor.

Usually, though, we pay it no attention. Even at the highest elevations, the presence of water in the atmosphere goes without saying. Those vast cloud banks seen from the jet liner's window are simply water vapor. Jet liners–now there's proof of how absurd the idea of air too thin to hold water is–the sky, even far above the highest clouds, is peppered with airplanes cleverly suspended by the use of air's weight and density. Too thin to hold water, indeed!

Yet I ask you to hear me out for at least two reasons. First of all, I *have* to tell the story. I *had* this Vision. I'm not making it up. I don't understand it at all but there is *so* much in this world that no one understands. Why let that stop us from discussing it?

Secondly, what if it's true? After trying for two decades, I still haven't found any solid evidence to convince me that the Vision was a lie. On the contrary, the more I study what *is* known, the more I'm convinced that what I saw is not only possible, but entirely plausible.

Not So Crazy

For instance, consider the planet Mars. The recent Mars Rover missions have proven there was once abundant liquid water on that planet–quite possibly even an ocean. But now Mars has almost no surface water at all, and what remains is frozen. There may well be water underground, but even that's not 100% certain. Further, any liquid water on the surface of Mars could not remain fluid for long, even if the planet were much warmer than it is. The boiling point of water is a function of both heat and pressure. Because of the low atmospheric pressure, water would rapidly evaporate on Mars if the temperature was even only barely above freezing, for temperatures we would consider quite cold would be warm enough to bring water to a rapid boil.

Abundant liquid water on Mars implies it was once both much warmer and had a far denser atmosphere than it does today.

No one knows what caused Mars to chill or to lose either its water or most of its air. One theory suggests Mars lost its magnetosphere some 4 billion years ago and then, over time, the solar wind eroded away the atmosphere. Presumably with the atmosphere went the surface water. Such a scenario would apparently represent no cause for alarm on Earth, being both inapplicable to us because we have a strong magnetosphere and innocuous because of the time frame.

But the *means* of Mars' loss of either atmosphere or water is *not* the issue. I am not concerned so much about *how* Mars lost all those critical components of a more friendly climate as *the fact* that it lost them. Nor am I particularly reassured by time estimates in the billions of years: I fail to see either the certainty of our knowledge of the processes involved, or that such knowledge would necessarily offer us any reason for complacency.

If Mars lost its water, then so could Earth. Yet *the* most basic assumption hydrologists make about Earth's water cycle is that it is closed, i.e., that water on this planet never escapes, but instead constantly cycles from ocean to atmosphere back to ocean again. However, no studies have been conducted to confirm this assumption.[5] Instead of red flags being raised by the strange loss of water on Mars, we heedlessly continue to assume that "it can't happen here."

By exactly the same logic, moreover, if Mars lost its atmosphere, then we shouldn't be so smug about ours. The extreme fluctuation in ambient temperature by Mars should also cause grave concern as we face observable shifts in our own.

In 1986 I had a Vision of doom. You, presumably, did not. For you to fully understand the potential danger without that insight, you should understand two related ideas: autocatalytic processes and catastrophe theory. Autocatalytic processes are a widely known phenomenon from chemistry. Catastrophe theory

---

[5] "No studies" is perhaps overreaching. But I have made numerous inquiries of scientists at J.P.L., Cal Tech, and elsewhere, without any responses indicating anything other than that the number of studies is zero. Meanwhile, several meteorologists confirmed my claim that closure is the base line assumption. But perhaps my credentials have not seemed adequate to some of those queried to justify response, as a number have not responded at all. Those who have, however, are uniformly unaware of any specific research to which I could go. My conjecture on the non-responses, by the way, is that they just thought the question too silly. Why they might think that is discussed later, at "Why the Einsteins Don't Get This" in Chapter 4.

is a much less well known subset of topology, itself a somewhat arcane field of mathematics.[6]

Catastrophe theory governs many, if not most, physical phenomena. Basically, it is the observation that a multitude of minor variations may, over time, amass enough influence on a system to cause a sudden, "catastrophic," effect. It's like climbing the back side of a mountain which has a cliff face: If you do it in the dark, despite never having made any significant jump upward on the ascent, you may find yourself suddenly in a long free fall as you take that last step off the edge.

But "catastrophic" in the mathematical context is not quite the same as in the common vernacular, for it actually only means "discontinuous," i.e., a very sudden change of some sort. To the mathematician, the event–the phenomenon of "discontinuity"–is the same whether it is huge or small. Mathematically, a fall is a catastrophe whether it is of 1000 feet or an inch. Hence, a "catastrophe" may mean what you would normally expect when encountering the word, or simply minor, common events, such as combustion, crystallization, evaporation, precipitation, or slipping on ice.

An autocatalytic process is something quite different. Catalysts are agents which facilitate some process, usually chemical, without themselves being consumed or diminished. So, for example, a catalytic converter is a device containing certain special metals (usually platinum and palladium) which facilitate chemical reactions in an automobile's exhaust system. This greatly increases the effectiveness of the vehicle's

---

[6]For a popular introduction to Catastrophe Theory see *The Scientific American*, March 1976, p. 234.

pollution control system, but, because the metals do not themselves get consumed in the process, little maintenance is required. Many chemical reactions won't even occur in the absence of an appropriate catalyst.

An *auto*catalytic process is any kind of activity which produces circumstances and/or products that enhance or reinforce its own process–one that acts as a catalyst to itself. A great many natural phenomena are autocatalytic, and, if not checked by some external factor, obey the classic mathematical law of exponential growth. In popular contexts, autocatalytic processes are often referred to as "positive feedback loops."

A few examples may clarify the differences and the relationship between these two ideas.

Behind my house there was once a popular bike riding spot where the local children could get a good jump from a hill ending with a gentle landing. For several years they took advantage of this feature, creating a well-packed trail marking their pleasure. Then one spring we had a downpour and, in a matter of minutes, the trail became a gully. Erosion is almost always catastrophic in the sense that, usually following a long period of quiescence, it happens quite suddenly. But it isn't fundamentally autocatalytic, since it depends on an outside source (e.g., rain) to trigger and maintain it.

Population growth, on the other hand, is basically autocatalytic because as the size of the population grows, the increased population tends to add to the size of the growth. The more critters there are, the easier it is for two critters to get together (in the Biblical sense). For example, when a population which is first observed at 1000, say, doubles every year (a constant *rate* of growth) the *actual* growth in numbers is 1000 in the first year, 2000 in the next, then 4000, 8000, 16000, etc. Hence the population growth in the fifth year is 16000, compared to only 1000 in the first year, and the original colony of 1000 will have bloomed to 32,000. Yet no individual in the population is procreating any more frequently than at the start. If you are not already familiar with the idea, suffice it to say that, even though they don't strictly represent the mathematical idea of discontinuity, and therefore aren't actually "catastrophes," autocatalytic phenomena may yet "blow up in your face," which, for our purposes, would essentially represent the same thing as a discontinuity.

As an example of how these two ideas may interact, the normal growth of algae in a lake is autocatalytic, but not catastrophic, largely thanks to the moderating influence of the numerous creatures that feed on the algae. Should something fall out of balance, such as the abrupt disappearance of the algivores, a sudden bloom of algae occurs. We'd then be looking at a phenomenon which, for our purposes, is both autocatalytic and catastrophic.

As a final example, the basic physics behind the atomic bomb relies on the fact that certain elements, such as uranium, naturally decay into lighter elements, releasing a tiny amount of energy as each atom of the mother element breaks into two or more smaller atoms of the new elements. Under proper conditions, this natural deterioration of heavy atoms into lighter ones can be manipulated into an autocatalytic process. The trick of nuclear warfare is creating these conditions. The idea is to slam a bunch of highly radioactive ("weapons grade") uranium or plutonium together to create, for just an instant, an autocatalytic chain reaction of these little releases of energy. As the process accelerates, the release of energy increases exponentially until it literally tears the uranium or plutonium supply, and everything else within a mile or so, apart. It takes less than a second or two to go from a little energy being released naturally to "ka-boom." Hence a nuclear explosion is a classic example of a process which, because it is autocatalytic, becomes catastrophic–and so quickly that it is mere pedantry to try to distinguish when and where these two phenomena begin to coincide.

Okay, here's a caveat: that's how the "little" bombs that destroyed Hiroshima and Nagasaki worked. They were fission, or atomic, bombs (A-bombs). All this explanation applies only to A-bombs. The only thing I know about hydrogen, or H-bombs, is that they use A-bombs to set them off: that is, the disastrous bombs of Hiroshima and Nagasaki serve today as mere blasting caps for the more modern version of nuclear insanity. So, you see, Hiroshima and Nagasaki *were* "little."

Technically, events in the real world are rarely, if ever, discontinuous. As the last example illustrates, however, there may be little reason to make a distinction in any case. Consequently, the mathematical definition of "catastrophe" is routinely fudged to make the idea of practical use. In a sense, this makes it easier to decide what is and isn't a catastrophe. You simply apply some subjective assessment as to whether the "suddenness" of the event is sufficient to warrant the terminology.

Hence, when the Larsen B ice shelf, some 3250 square kilometers of ice 200 meters thick, resting on the ocean and covering a bay between two peninsulas, suddenly disintegrated in the Antarctic's summer of 2001-2002, I'd call it catastrophic despite the fact it actually took the better part of a month to collapse completely. An ice shelf is, really, a geologic entity, and such a time span is literally instantaneous in geologic terms.

By contrast, whether or not a process is autocatalytic may be a most complicated question and no amount of "fudging" makes the analysis easier. Global warming, for instance, is expected to shrink the polar ice caps significantly, thereby reducing the planet's ability to reflect sunlight and increasing its tendency to absorb the sun's heat. That would suggest it may be auto catalytic.

But a warmer Earth might also be more hospitable to greenery over a wider zone than is currently the case, which, presumably, would make for more efficient recycling of CO_2[7] out of the atmosphere, dampening the global warming phenomenon.

Which influence dominates? What other significant factors are there? Clearly, there are many. Complex systems cannot be analyzed without complex analytical approaches which are, inherently, fraught with uncertainties.

Just to complicate matters more, many normal processes may be "pushed" toward autocatalytic status by external factors. The predators' influence in the algae example above is illustrative. In such circumstances catastrophe often results, for there is a point beyond which nothing will stop the process from rapidly consuming all resources available. A keen observer can usually recognize when such a situation is pending, but why, how severe the event will be, or when to expect the "discontinuity," are more often opaque. We appear to be already on the verge of such phenomena with global

---

[7]carbon dioxide

warming, the depletion of ozone, and the disappearance of natural habitats.

In addition, humans routinely engage in innumerable activities, such as our incessant conversion of electrical energy into BTU's[8], which we have not even begun to look at seriously in the context of global impacts. For example, the rise in popularity of air conditioning represents a huge source of artificial heat being created by humans. Even if global warming is not *inherently* autocatalytic overall, some of the associated impacts tend in that direction (the hotter it is the more we want to use the air conditioner). Will any of these practices and/or their byproducts impact the air or water economies? Not only has no one answered these questions, so far as I can ascertain,[9] most have not even been asked.

We know that something is very wrong with the global environment, and there will be consequences. But how severe, exactly when and what to expect is entirely uncertain. It's well-established that human activity is affecting the global economy of the atmosphere by altering its physical content; Industry has changed the relative amounts of both CFCs[10] and CO_2 in the atmosphere significantly enough so as to have the observable impacts of ozone depletion and global warming.

---

[8] British Thermal Units: a measure of heat

[9] See footnote 5 page 2-29

[10] chlorofluorocarbons, the chemical compound implicated in ozone depletion

What we don't know, however, is whether these, or anything else we are doing, might be altering the most important aspects of the global economies of either H_2O or the atmosphere–their volumes. Our *assumption* is that both are constants. But we don't actually know that, because we have not done experiments to verify this antiquated axiom of meteorology, at least not since our population has grown so large as to make the question truly worthy of consideration[11]. In view of what we now know about Mars' global atmospheric and hydrologic economies, not asking the question strikes me as extraordinarily reckless.

Here's the truly frightening prospect: if we are engaged in activities that deplete either water or atmosphere, then whether those activities are autocatalytic and how soon we recognize that are critical to whether stopping the total depletion of either resource will be possible.

Humankind has thrown nature far off balance. We probably don't even recognize all the subsystems we have already seriously affected. Consequently, whether the system will re-stabilize, and where or when, is impossible to say. The system is simply far too complex.

A Modest Proposal:
Ask The Right Questions!

In the presence of the Mars Rovers' strong evidence indicating that the baseline mass of both water and atmosphere on a planet may fluctuate vastly, we are absurdly naive to continue assuming that Earth's are constants and dangerously cavalier to assume that any

---

[11]See footnote 5 page 2-29

changes necessitate geologic time to have an impact. *Especially so* in the presence on Earth of the global changes we've already recognized. We ought to be anxiously testing those assumptions.

What we're doing in reaction instead is asking, "Was there once life on Mars?" and "Might it still be there?" Some believe that, in the presence of water on Mars, there certainly would have also been life. I tend to agree, but what we *should* be asking is far more urgent: "if Mars lost its habitability, how do we avoid precisely the same catastrophe on Earth?"

At least it seems like that's a more important question from my perspective. I am, after all, an inhabitant of *this* planet.

Humans assume that our planet's history, and not that of Mars, will be the model for our future. We cannot see Mars' fate as a potential model of our own tragedy. Yet, if we truly believe that humankind is wrecking this world with the disasters we've perpetrated on the environment, we should. Global warming, acid rain, and toxic pollution should prompt more serious questions than "How high will the oceans get?" or "Will we have to wear sunglasses?"

People, we could drown out here! We've got to stop calling for help in the polite, "give us a hand" way.

What blinds us to the more important question of, "Just how far out of balance might this go?" is our own human-centeredness. We are in the most basic form of denial: because God *made* it for us, the Earth is special.[12] It is natural that we should be in denial. Ignoring death is a tried and true way of enjoying life.

---

[12]more on this shortly

And the death of a planet–our planet–is simply too horrible to contemplate in any case. But when mankind begins to have global impact–something entirely unique in Earth's history–we must consider the probability that the effects will be equally unique.

That's *not* so crazy.

We ought to immediately ask whether humanity's unprecedented global impacts might be the first domino in a chain of events with truly catastrophic results. The questions ought to be far greater than, "What impact will higher temperatures have on glaciation and coastal plains?" or, "Will increased temperatures affect crop yields?"

It is reasonable to expect global phenomena to have global consequences. We need to urgently ask, "Will there be an impact on the atmosphere's ability to retain water, or on earth's ability to retain its atmosphere?" or even, "If injecting chemicals such as CFCs has such serious consequences, what other global impacts are our various waste products having?"

These are questions scientists need to examine posthaste. It ought not require a Vision to stimulate interest in such things. Even the lower-case kind of vision should be more than sufficient. The results from the Mars Rovers should be adequate motivation to ask the question, "Why couldn't something like that happen here" and to move us to monitor *all* aspects of our planet's ecosystem.

Now I need to clarify something. Here, I have speculated using hypothetical and cautionary language. I chose to do so because I dread losing readers due to my "obviously delusional" ranting. But, in *my* mind, these are *not* mere hypotheticals. My motivation is more visceral than mere intellectual arguments. The fact is: I had/saw a Vision. A fact I pray will resonate with you, dear reader. No amount of effort on our part will "save the planet." The death of Earth is assured–and all too soon. While no specific time was specified in the Vision, it was certain on this point: Life on this planet is *already* doomed. All Life. The *exact* means of its demise is not at all clear to me. But that *was* the Vision. I have given up resisting it for being what it is. I am no longer "arguing with God."

Here, I've presented the rational arguments supporting my belief for the benefit of those who may doubt spirituality even more than I once did. Don't dismiss me too readily. Our best scientists are making my point ever more forcefully.

Almost Moses

"Ah ha!!" you say. "Got you now. This guy really believes in this "Vision" thing. How crazy is that?" Maybe I don't sleep in doorways and bum cigarettes and small change for a living, but I clearly believe in this paranormal experience. Well, let's look at that for a few paragraphs.

What do we know about Visions? Not much, actually. Even I, despite having had one, cannot begin to explain what it was, where it came from, or how it happened. I *can* say this: whether it seems real to you or not, it was certainly real to me. I sat on it for two decades and it is still as vivid as the day it happened. It was a change is my reality. It was a phenomenon which I have never experienced either before or since.

Of course, we know that a number of important people have claimed to have had Visions–and here I remind you we are speaking of the metaphysical kind of Vision, not the common "vision" that virtually *all* important people claim to have. That kind usually has something to do with how someone equally important can make more money.

Unfortunately, we also know that a great many very unimportant people claim to have seen Visions. Fifteen minutes on the streets of any major city is likely to bring you in contact with at least one such person (although its much more difficult to identify them now that everyone seems to be talking to themselves as they walk about with cell phones to their ears).

My Vision had no preceding context or trigger. Nothing I had done caused it. It was *not* induced. When you are just biking along through Europe, minding your own business, living your own life, having a wonderful time, and suddenly you are transported to the end of the world–it is not merely "an hallucination." It was as real as if I had been hit by a drunk driver. I neither saw it coming nor expected it, but it was real. It was . . . well, a *Vision*. Trying to cope with having had it has been the dominant theme of my life ever since. At first I tried to deny, now I accept and promulgate.

And so it shall be when I die.

A Vision is compelling and conveys huge amounts of information, certainly, but the one I saw, at least, had frustratingly unclear aspects. While unambiguous in the fact of its *being* a Vision, it was infuriatingly open to interpretation as to what I was to *do* about it. Or even how I was supposed to go about doing *any*thing about it.

In thinking about Visions, Moses has to come to mind. His Vision is legend. It was also contained in the part of the Bible I managed to get through during my devout period as a youth when I set "read it all" as a personal goal.

Here's how I remember the story:

Moses was raised by royalty (the Pharaoh) but was banished when his Jewish origins were discovered. (All of this is dangerously contaminated, by the way, with memories from the Cecile B. DeMille classic movie, *The Ten Commandments,*[13] starring Charlton Heston, so please forgive any minor inaccuracies.) One morning following his exile, while tending sheep or some such solitary activity, Moses comes upon a bush which is burning brightly, but which is not consumed by the fire. He approaches and hears the voice of God telling him to free His people. Moses does nothing about the Vision at first, finding all kinds of excuses, including the fact that he is a very poor speaker (perhaps even speech impaired?). This is one point Cecile definitely took liberty with: Moses was no Charlton Heston (nor vice versa if you think on it).

Anyway, God provides Aaron, Moses' own brother, as a mouthpiece, and arms Moses with a powerful little walking stick that performs miracles. Then God shoves him into the fray–or maybe he goes, reluctantly, on his own, I forget. He struggles quite successfully, using his powerful, murderous staff to strike a little respect into the Pharaoh, who, like all heads of state, was pretty headstrong.

After numerous demonstrations of God's power (pestilence, plague, etc.), Moses threatens to kill the firstborn children (sons?) of anyone in the land not sufficiently frightened to show subservience by killing a lamb and pouring its blood on the doorsill. The Angel of Death passes over such households, and thus Pharaoh

---

[13]*The Ten Commandments*, Directed by Cecile B. DeMille, Paramont Pictures 1956

loses his heir and one of the more sacred holidays on the Jewish calendar gets its name.

After Pharaoh yields to Moses' demands, however, he suffers remorse at the decision and pursues the fleeing Israelites. The refugees take an unorthodox, but effective, shortcut across the Red Sea, and strike out into the desert unhindered, only to get lost for a very long time. At one point, they desperately need food, and God sends it in the form of "manna" falling from the sky. At another, they are dying of thirst and God tells Moses to command a stone to spring forth with water. For unexplained reasons, Moses suddenly seems to suffer a lack of faith, manifested by hesitancy at the image of his speaking to a stone in front of all those people. Maybe they'd been lost just a little too long and Moses feared the troops were already getting second thoughts about the sanity of their leader. Maybe it was the stuttering thing. Who knows?

Anyway, Moses smites the stone with the magical staff instead. That works, but it pisses God off that, after all He had done for him, Moses would have the gall to be afraid to follow His every instruction to the letter. God was, apparently, premenstrual during the entire period covered by the Old Testament. As punishment, Moses is forbidden entry to the Promised Land. He dies looking across the Jordan, never seeing the final fruit of his labor.

I have come to see many parallels between Moses' story and my own situation. For one thing, Moses' reluctance to immediately get up and rush into the fight: he seems to have spent a long time agonizing over such questions/reactions as "Why the hell did you pick me, Lord?", or, "I'm not the one you really meant to have stumble across your little phone booth in the wild;" or, "Look, I'm kind of busy trying to adjust to being banished, poor, and alone here. I've got a life, okay?"

Perhaps I project. But that's how Moses' delay in hopping to the task strikes me. I've asked myself a thousand times, "Why the hell would God pick *me*?" It makes no sense whatsoever.

But, maybe He didn't pick *me*. Or Moses, for that matter.

Maybe the bush wasn't the only phone booth in the wild, or Moses the only one who noticed it sitting there on that barren little hill, ringing its hot little leaves off. Maybe God didn't *choose* Moses so much as Moses rose to the occasion.

Perhaps a Vision is like a T.V. set in the window of some store showing the news. Most of us just walk by, hardly noticing. Some stop and watch, not able to figure out exactly what the content is; it isn't always easy to hear the voice through the glass, or over the crackle from the fire that isn't consuming the bush, or whatever. Some get the message full-force and wind up wandering the streets of a major city talking angrily to themselves. A few try to do something about the Vision and become totally forgotten waifs hanging from one of the thousands of wooden crosses that weren't situated on Cavalry on the first "Good Friday." Some do some good. Some do more harm than good. Visions are, I suspect, not particularly forgiving of incompetence or lack of faith.

Most of us, if we see the T.V. set at all, just ignore it. We walk right on by—on our way to work, got a date tonight, about to buy or sell a house, or some crack, or whatever we have in our myopic little sights for that day.

But, occasionally, the T.V. in the window is seen by a Moses. Someone who, for whatever reasons, not only notices, but pulls it off, actually realizing the task that God has set. Someone with the connections, education, and the social training of an adopted son of Pharaoh, perhaps. Or someone who just gets lucky. But one thing seems certain: God–whatever that term means, and I am making no pretense to know–sets large tasks, and the faint of heart aren't apt to succeed in performing them. When someone sees the task and succeeds in accomplishing it, we remember him or her. We assume the Vision was his/hers alone, completely ignoring the numerous nut-cases, would-be revolutionaries, prophets and malcontents who followed the exact same Vision to ignominious deaths. God spoke to Moses. Maybe God also spoke to Jahosephat and Hadassa and Billy, but Joe didn't do anything about it, Hadassa was only an unempowered woman, and Bill was the wrong race at the wrong time.

Maybe we simply don't know enough about Visions to realize that they don't just happen to individuals. Maybe they're broadcast, not beamed. Maybe there are thousands of people who've passed the T.V. but didn't notice it, recognize it for what is was, or just dismissed it as irrelevant to them. Others have noticed and know as surely as do I, although perhaps not so vividly, that we *are* killing this planet. These people recognize that the reason humans aren't solving the world's problems is that humans *are* the world's problem. People like you, perhaps. People whose attention I want to attract, for, despite what you may now think, we *do* have some options.

I think I may know, however, why we all hold so strongly to the idea that Moses, or Abraham, or Christ, or Mohammed, or any of the many others who've seen and followed Visions to successful conclusions, were God's specific targets. Fact is, when you've concentrated on the Message, when you've really gotten it, it *feels* like it was directed specifically at you. So you tend to talk about it as being "your Vision." Too often, I do it myself.

Unfortunately, that impression is reinforced by the many who do not stop and look at the T.V. in the window at all. Not having seen or heard the Message themselves, they dismiss the ones who've grasped more than they, but perhaps not the complete version, as being alarmists. The more fully you comprehend, the more likely they are to discount you as having "talked to God."

Ridicule is a very powerful tool for maintaining the status quo and discouraging visionaries of all sorts from suggesting bothersome improvements. To the extent that I sometimes fall into the trap of personalizing the Vision merely because of how cathartic the realization was for me, I apologize to those of you who have, thus far, seen only parts of the story, but recognize the danger. I do you disservice by opening us all up to charges of irrational extremism.

I saw a Vision. But it was not exclusively mine, even though I sometimes don't catch myself when I talk as if it were. People all around the world have been glimpsing the same revelation.

The problems the vision addressed are extreme, and extreme responses are called for. My role isn't to try to set myself up as a Messenger from God. The Message is out there for everyone to see for himself. You need no intermediary. You only need to look and listen.

Maybe my role can be to turn up the volume on the T.V. so that more of us will be able to figure it out.

Maybe I can be the extra little nudge you need to get up and do something about it. Maybe I can make some of you look more closely at the screen, despite how very unappealing the show is–this all-too-real "reality show." Maybe you just haven't looked at the screen long enough yet to have seen the end of the Vision–the way out that is only revealed in the second part, and which is our only real hope.

If my experience is typical, an inherent part of having seen a Vision is that one comes away from it with a Mission. Specifically, the second part of the Vision was a Command. I've found that I can't ignore it any more. I must pursue it. But fulfilling the Command will be something far beyond what I can accomplish alone, or even in my lifetime. My role and yours, if you choose to join me, is to get the project started. The harder part–the truly hard part–will come in the remote future. The second part of the Vision sets a task that none of us–not from my generation or the next or the next–will see completed in their lifetimes. It is a work that, like the great temples of the ancient world, will be hundreds of years in the building.

What we need now is for all those who've already seen the truth of the first part of the Vision to come alive. To come together and seize the moment–to adopt the Vision as their own, personal, Vision. Like Moses' people, it is time to rise up.

Moses? Moses?!!

When I've shared these thoughts with others, I've sometimes gotten an interesting response; "You think you're like Moses?"

My reaction to such a sentiment varies with my mood at the time. Sometimes I simply can't get over the degree to which the questioner doesn't get it. I'm talking about Visions here, not about Moses–nor even his Vision. Just about how we *regard* Visions. Besides, this is not about *me*. It's not even about *us*. Didn't I already mention that?

This was a *Vision* I saw. Whether or not Moses had a Vision, or whether hundreds of others also had Moses' Vision, or how my experience compares to his–none of these questions strike me as particularly helpful to dwell upon. That was, like, five millennia ago, for pity's sake! I'm not trying to upstage Moses. I'm not *that* crazy.

The Vision set me on a Mission. A Mission which contains a very small element of hope. But it's not at all apparent that humankind will benefit from that small bit of encouraging news. Our species' survival in the ordeal that awaits us all–that awaits all living creatures–may, in fact, be pretty unlikely. The survival of green algae beyond the death of this planet will be difficult enough to achieve. If humans manage to get through this at all, I believe there will almost certainly be no collective memory of our era. Talking about me or Moses will be a lot like discussing who first learned to control fire. So what significance does whether or not I'm comparing myself to Moses have? Hell, when the Earth is dead, nobody's going to know about either of us. The important thing here is that *something* from this planet survives. If you had seen the death of Earth's Lifeforce, as I have, you'd understand that.

If you can imagine it, you can understand it.

The second part of the Vision suggests a possible means of *some*thing surviving. But I care not whether those survivors remember me or recognize my contributions at all. What I care about–the *only* thing I care about–is that we find some way to guarantee the survival of *some* living thing from this planet.

Once you've realized, as I have, the tragedy the death of the Lifeforce would be, nothing but guaranteeing its survival in some form is important.

Then the Vision will be yours, too.

Know Nothings

A strange story of the rescue of a young girl from an automobile wreck seems pertinent to me here. It happened on U.S. Highway 50 in 1999 and was widely reported in the local news, where I followed the story. A car had gone off the road and down a cliff. It was after dark and no one witnessed the accident, nor could the wrecked vehicle be seen by traffic above. There were three people in the car, a couple and their young daughter. The couple was killed, but the daughter survived. She was rescued after the sheriff's department received a report later that evening, apparently completely unrelated, that a naked woman was seen walking alongside the highway in what turned out to be the same locale. On investigating, they found no woman, but one of the officers, Rich Strasser, returned the next morning, noticed skid marks and found the wreck and surviving child. The incident occurred miles from the nearest house, so coincidence seems very unlikely. Did the woman who reported the naked lady to the police see the mother's ghost? *What* then?

Prior to having the Vision, I was always one of those people most skeptical of the paranormal. By that I don't mean that I rejected it out of hand, but rather that I had seen no personal evidence of it and I tended to doubt stories about "psychic" experiences. Since the Vision I have not been so sure. I believe there is such a thing as "sight." Whether it lies in the Visionary who has a special ability to see things others do not–like the woman who reported the naked lady to the police–or is

2-48

something which some people can manifest and project–here presumably either the girl or her dead mother–I don't know. I don't know whether I believe in ghosts or not, for *I've* never seen one, as far as I know (would one know, for sure?). But I definitely now believe there are things that cannot be explained without resorting to the paranormal.

To be honest, though, I've long felt this to be a possibility. In college, I worked for a time with deaf children. I developed a great sympathy for that particular handicap. It is usually a far more cruel curse, at least if carried from birth, than blindness, for it isolates a child from the hearing world in profound ways which are not evident to the casual observer. A deaf child in a hearing world is estranged from everyone around him/her. The frustration of not being able to communicate is a burden that hearing people cannot imagine and one the blind do not share with the deaf. Most people have no idea. The situation is frequently psychologically devastating.

What is, perhaps, cruelest is that it is so totally unnecessary. Deafness itself need not be a serious handicap at all. Deaf children raised where signing is common are as happy and well-adjusted as normal children, for partial isolation from a hearing world is not nearly as debilitating as being cut off from everyone. The issue is communication, not how it is done. The inability to hear would not be considered a severe handicap at all if only a few of us were capable of hearing in the first place.

Between one and two percent of the general population is deaf, i.e., in a town of 100,000, there are between 1000 and 2000 deaf individuals. They are largely invisible because most of them have learned to avoid drawing attention to themselves; the hearing population is largely prejudiced against them, and can be, especially as children, quite cruel, even if unintentionally so.

Imagine what the world would be like if this figure were reversed, or even more dramatically, reversed and exaggerated, so that only one or two tenths of a percent, say, were capable of hearing? Certainly we would all communicate via signing. But, more interestingly, wouldn't there be a similar pressure on the few who could hear to make themselves inconspicuous? Wouldn't the ability to hear appear to the deaf majority almost exactly as the (supposed) ability to perceive via ESP appears to those of us who've never known it? The few hearing people might eventually come to deny, even to themselves, their own perceptions most of the time. Only when suddenly startled by some loud sound would they reveal themselves. Hearing people would likely be explained away as just being super-sensitive. But normally those who could hear would be virtually invisible. Their abilities would probably be a matter of some speculation and disbelief amongst the vast majority of the population.

Despite my natural tendency toward skepticism of people who claim extraordinary abilities, such as channelers and psychics, this line of thinking leaves me open to the idea that they may simply have an ability which, until the Vision, I seemed to lack. On the one hand, I still doubt most people who claim to have psychic powers. There is, after all, a certain market for the histrionics they tend to display and that, in itself, invites pretenders. I am, however, no longer dubious of the existence of methods of communication beyond our normal perceptions.

Besides, am I to pretend I did not perceive what I, in fact, did, simply because most people apparently didn't hear or see it? I was given an insight that I have not been able to refute via rational analysis–a skill at which I excel. I must respond to it.

Reluctance

That was not my initial reaction, however. I had hardly perceived the Vision before I began to doubt. Over and over, I asked, "What *was* that?" Surely an hallucination, I thought. Yet I was sure it wasn't. I could find no cause for it, nor explain where the content might have originated. The idea of the entire Earth dying simply seemed too, well, *big*, for it to have been mine. True, I'd thought about nuclear war numerous times, and had even read novels such as Doris Lessing's *Memoirs of a Survivor*[14], and Nevil Shute's *On the Beach*[15] and nonfiction speculations such as Jonathan Shell's *The Fate of the Earth*[16]. But none of these ever approached the kind of stark, unmitigated, numbing, horror that had come to me in the flash of an instant.

Even Biblical and ministerial messages were something altogether different from the view I'd received directly from whoever, or better, whatever, it is that apparently dispenses Visions. Religious doom is always about man's relationship with God. Humanness was not, *in any way* a factor in the Vision. Besides, I'd

---

[14] Doris Lessing, *Memoirs of a Survivor*, Alfred Knopf, New York, N.Y., 1975

[15] Nevil Shute, *On the Beach,* Willim Heinemann, London, England, 1957

[16] Jonathan Shell, *The Fate of the Earth*, Alfred Knopf, New York, N.Y., 1982

long before abandoned the belief that "God" pays any individualized attention to our species at all. I just assumed that humans, like the dinosaurs, had come and would eventually, just go. But the Earth? It's the only life we know, for sure, to exist. I couldn't have imagined *all* life "just going."

By way of trying to convince myself that the Message was simply insane, I diligently endeavored to establish it's absurdity. I thought by doing so I would be able to dismiss the "hallucination" for the delusion it was, putting the whole episode behind me.

But this approach simply backfired. The evidence wouldn't cooperate. Researching the scientific literature convinced me that, not only was there nothing to debunk the Vision, but rather the facts and theories supported it.

About Depression

Before continuing with my story, though, I need to talk about depression. Dealing with depression is something you will have to learn to do, if we are to realize the promise and the hope of the second part of the Vision. Besides searching diligently for contrary evidence, my major preoccupation for at least the first 15 years following the Vision was coping with a massive depression. It's nothing like that today, but it certainly still comes up. There's evidently plenty to be depressed about. Environmental news assaults me every day in ways most people can only vaguely perceive. The Vision always weighs on me.

What sustains me is the certain knowledge that I, and all of us, are blessed beyond description. Having seen the Earth without its life, I am far more appreciative of how wonderful that life is than ever I was before. This is *truly* Heaven on Earth. And I don't just mean the beautiful parts of the Earth, nor even just the peaceful parts. I mean *everywhere* on Earth. There is nowhere on the surface of this planet that Life does not thrive. That's mythically marvelous. A wonder so great that even wars don't really dent it. Try never to lose sight of this fact: Life *is* wondrous and *we* are a part of it. That alone is cause to celebrate. Celebrating Life salves the spirit.

Having the knowledge of that wonderment makes it not only possible, but really a duty, to enjoy the blessings we've been given. Only by seeing it *all* gone can you truly realize how lucky we are, even those in the most dire of circumstances. Celebration must be a large part of who we are.

When you first realize how horrible the idea of the loss of Life really is, a deep depression will likely seize you. When you see the truth of the Vision, *expect* to be depressed. That is one of the five stages of grief that Elisabeth Kubler-Ross describes[17]. The stages are denial, anger, bargaining, depression, and acceptance. I don't know whether you're supposed to go through them in order or not, but for me, depression seemed to be the first and certainly the longest lasting. But it has largely faded in the face of the Mission set by the Vision, and by the appreciation of my–and our–good fortune at living here and now. As you are about to see, it is our generation's lot only to start the ball rolling. It is a ball rolling toward a dubious opportunity for survival, nothing more. But we, here and now, can still revel in the joys of this planet. We are actually obligated to enjoy our blessings, for without a much greater

---

[17]See Elisabeth Kubler-Ross' *On Death and Dying,* Touchstone, New York, N.Y., 1969

appreciation of what we have, mankind will only hasten the loss. *Enjoy* those things we have, mind you–not *destroy* them.

And now, finally, let's talk about that little bit of hope.

Chapter 3
Banishment

The Vision (2): The Call

So, where is the hope in this horrendous Vision that begins with *"We're not going to make it;"* and apparently offers no mitigation in that assessment? Wouldn't it be a Message more worthy of concealing than revealing? What is the practical value of adding to our misery by sharing this if there is no hope at all? Isn't it merely cruel and perverse?

There *was* a second part to the Vision, however. Not a repudiation of the first, but a Message of hope nonetheless. I've spent the years since 1986 not only confirming the likelihood of the dire prediction in the first part but also investigating the possibilities in the second part.

This was the Message, in toto, both parts of which had equal strength: *"We're not going to make it. We've got to get off."*

As with the first part, the second's aural content was accompanied by a transcendent comprehension of its full meaning. Trying to communicate how this realization came about is, quite literally, impossible. The closest analogue to ordinary cognition I can think of is the idea of a "memory dump" from computer science. The entire experience was like being on the receiving end of a "mind dump" from some superior, unfathomable intelligence. Beyond the eleven words and actually seeing the death on the hill, there was no intermediating perception of any kind–no logic, no train of thought: just immediate, total, complete knowledge. Knowledge it will take a lifetime to fully explain, if I succeed at all.

Instantaneously I knew we have to leave the planet, that part was transparent. But also that "we," throughout the Message, is not a reference inclusive only of human beings. It references the Lifeforce itself. I recognized a oneness in the word "we" I had never seen before and that word will never again have the same limited scope of its prior meaning for me. The ants and I, the birds, the fishes, the trees, the mold, the viruses...all of *it*... and I, are "we." If *any* remnant of life from Earth is to survive past the death of the planet–the imminence of which was a central portion of the first part–it will be through its having abandoned this ship, Earth, for another. Or, what is equivalent, by its having been sent abroad by some means such as our (humans) having intentionally seeded another planet with life that originated here.

A Reality Check (1):
How appropriate–or not–is this?

When most people hear me talk about "getting off the planet," they immediately jump to conclusions. The most common is that we will certainly be an interplanetary species eventually, so what's the problem? Some think the solution I'm proposing is completely unrelated to the problem I'm trying to address. Another common instant response is that the proposed solution is a diversion from working on the problem and can only interfere with efforts to improve our situation.

That so many have pre-prepared responses is not surprising. "The end is near" is not a particularly revolutionary idea and most people have thought about the possibility at some time or another. It's a common theme in religious teachings. Religious predictions, however, concerned exclusively with the human soul, pay little or no attention to concerns about plants or animals, which was a central theme in my Vision.

Science fiction scenarios and secular scientific predictions, concerned with nuclear war, the decline of civil society, pandemics etc., also tend to be uniformly human-centered. Not being human-centric, I guess the Vision's first part is pretty radical.

"We've got to get off," as a response is also novel in the context of "the end is near." It's a very large jump which, at first, appears to be absurd. If it could be done at all, surely it would require a time frame that would rule it out as any kind of response to environmental degradation.

Besides, if going into space is the solution, why not just fix Earth? That *must* be easier. For one thing, Earth is closer, and that way *everyone*–every *species*, even–would benefit, not just those lucky few who were shipped off to the stars. All our resources are right here. This is where all of our technology is located. This is *home*, for God's sake. Why waste money and resources by throwing them away on outer space?

Unfortunately, this is the first widely held false premise, and probably the most important to discredit. The problem is that it *isn't* easier. In fact, it's quite impossible.

There's one simple fact that trumps all the arguments you're always hearing from all those optimists out there in the environmental movement crying out in their timid little voices that we've "got to *do* something," while simultaneously assuring us "there's still time."

That simple fact is that we humans are here. We're here *all over the place.* Anyone who thinks there is a chance of reining us in now is simply ignoring who we are, and how many of us there are. Even more importantly, ignoring how many more of us there are now than there were when you read the first "how many of us there are." Our population is already too big, and it's getting bigger all the time—at exponential rates.

It's humans who are driving the ecosystem in exactly the opposite direction from that in which it needs to go. The largest failing of the environmental movement is its insistence that there's still time, if only we start doing the right thing.

Logically, of course, that's a true statement. If we were to start doing the right thing, it *could* all be saved. But don't forget, I spent thirty years teaching mathematics. I understand logic better, even, than I do trains. While the logic of "do the right thing" is unassailable, it is also true that if wishes were horses then beggars would ride; if money didn't rule politics, you, my friend, would be President of the United States, and I would like caviar. If your uncle on your father's side is a monkey, then two plus two is three billion. All unassailably correct. Logically. An implication that begins with a false premise is *always* a "true statement."

But by the time humans, as a species, start "doing the right thing," horses will have mastered flight and will wish they were as good at it as the pigs.

Well, that may be a bit harsh, but it will be *far* too late, for sure.

Wait a minute: If my fear is that human population growth can't be stopped, am I trying to say the expansion of Homo sapiens' population is inevitable? What about AIDS Or Bird Flu? A recurrence of the Plague? What makes me so worried about the continued expansion of our population in the face of all these calamitous possibilities?

Well, I'm not sure about all that. Maybe we *will* see a reversal in human population trends brought about by some extra-human influence. The Vision said nothing at all about the possibility. And it most certainly *is* a possibility.

Historically, though, such a development would be brand new. The most famous of human setbacks came with the black plague of the Middle Ages and the flu pandemic at the end of World War I. Both had measurable impacts on world population, killing perhaps as many 1/5 to ⅓ of all humans (but surely not more). Yet the effect was only a glitch in the continuing overall dominance of Homo sapiens over all other species. It's good, in this context, to remember that while the bugs are killing us off, we are also reproducing, so the percent of the population killed off is largely offset by the reproduction the next year. In fact, it is usually the case that, on a worldwide scale, devastating epidemics may slow but almost never reverse *overall* population growth for more than a few years, at most.

AIDS, for example, has reportedly reversed population growth in all of Africa, and that certainly slows world population growth. But, worldwide, we continue to "advance." In recent years, a very conservative estimate of human population growth per year (1.2%) predicts 74 million more people next year than we have today. In total, about 30 million people are currently *infected* with the HIV virus throughout the entire planet, so the epidemic, as it currently stands, might slow our growth, but it will not likely result in a *decline* in the worldwide human population. Yet we cannot say for sure that it, or something even worse, won't do so in the future.

Still, what are the chances that any such problem will wind up putting humans in a position from which we won't recover within a generation or two?

Virtually nil.

The Earth should be so lucky. No, if Life here is to be saved, we can't count on the microbes to do it. It'll be up to us.

Whistling Past The Graveyard

Let me elaborate on why I have such a firm position on the "if we just start doing the right thing" arguments.

Immediately following the Vision, I went on a campaign of trying to "save the world." The Reagan administration was then in full assault on the environment and routinely issuing only slightly veiled threats of nuclear holocaust anytime relations with the Soviet Union got stickier than usual. The world had never been more obviously on the brink.

I started a local anti-nuclear weapons/environmental group, "Common Sense." My work with that group, although related to the Vision, served mainly to distract me from facing my Mission full on. But it did provide lessons I rely upon today.

One of the more pertinent to the current topic was the observation that virtually no environmentalist seems to actually believe the overwhelmingly negative content of the movement's predictions. Environmentalists are optimists, thinking recycling paper will save the forests, computers will lead to a paperless society, and reducing greenhouse gases will result in avoiding climate change.

They seek to stem the ill effects of human activity by saving species from extinction, preserving natural habitats, and keeping their own backyards from becoming noticeably unpleasant. Although monitoring global conditions has some currency, even most professional ecologists do not actually attempt to attack truly global problems. Or, if so, they seem only to couch their concerns in terms of the potential implications for human beings. There are, of course, some notable exceptions. However, few environmentalists embrace issues on the order of magnitude I am addressing. The scope of their concern is virtually always limited to sustainable this and sustainable that, and the bottom line of "sustainable" is always "sustains human beings." Every dire prediction is followed by a pronouncement of how it can still be avoided. Some of that may be due to the extraordinary pressure the publishing industry places on anyone wishing to enlist their services (who's going to buy a book with nothing but bad news?). But, to the extent it discourages honest discussion of the potential momentousness of our situation, such optimism gives the general public a false sense of security and does our movement great harm.

It is not surprising that environmentalists' primary concern is the impact human activities have on humans. That attitude is virtually universal amongst our species. But that global warming, for instance, only raises concerns on the order of "sea level increases" shows an extraordinarily myopic view of its potential impact. These are global problems. Global problems are going to have consequences far beyond those that merely affect Homo sapiens.

A Note of Panic

Most of us assume the ecosystem is robust enough to be independent of any one species' activities and that global changes take eons. But when humans can track our own global impacts, those assumptions are simply no longer justified. If, as the Vision predicts, we do lose our atmosphere and/or water, it will surely happen in a catastrophic manner, at least in relative terms. It wouldn't be a matter of an eon or two. More likely it will occur over only a few decades or, at most, a few centuries. Some impact of worldwide human activity will probably prove to be autocatalytic. The autocatalytic factors involved, because of their global scale, may be in place long before we recognize their presence. By the time we realize the deterioration, and acknowledge it, it will be too late to stop it. The process is very likely already in play. The time to ascertain whether our water supply or atmosphere, for example, are secure is *far* in advance of our accidentally noticing their atrophy while studying some otherwise innocuous aspect of the global ecology. The proper time was yesterday, not tomorrow or even today. Unless we consciously maintain a vigilance for potential threats, we risk being surprised by an oncoming juggernaut.

Even if detected early on, whether or not noticing such a large-scale problem as the loss of atmosphere would do any good is arguable. It depends on whether solutions are even attainable and on the degree to which humans would be inconvenienced by their implementation. We do not have a great track record with problems whose solutions involve personal sacrifice, or even restraint. Furthermore, if we perceive it as costing a lot of money, or hindering industry, the outlook is grim indeed. Preserving the temperate rain-forests, attaining zero population growth, controlling greenhouse gases, and correcting the hole in the ozone layer serve pretty well as examples of how unsuccessful we have, historically, been.[18]

Environmentalists must start demanding answers to questions such as, "Is this global warming thing autocatalytic and, if so, how far will it run?"

Crying Wolf in the Lion's Den

When I was in the water at Hole in the Wall wondering whether I needed rescuing and contemplating one more attempt at body surfing in, I opted to call for help. Had I waited for another wave I probably would have already been drawn out too far for my rescuer to reach me, and he probably would not have been in the water anyway. I'd have been beyond rescuing. Even then, at first, I was unconvincing because of how timid my cry was. So it is with environmentalists today. They are crying out to their fellow humans in that polite, "give us a hand," tone. Environmentalists are not convincing. What changed my tone in calling for help, and what led to my rescue, was my realization upon hearing myself that I didn't sound sincere. We environmentalists need

---

[18]The status of the Ozone Hole was touted as an example of an environmental success in Al Gore's popular movie, *An Inconvenient Truth*. A careful listen, however, reveals that the laudatory comments are actually directed at the production of CFC's, the chemicals believed to cause the depletion of Ozone. At this writing the Ozone Hole is still very much with us, and the next twenty years will be crucial to confirming whether the reductions in CFC's will result in the Ozone layer's recovery.

to listen to ourselves. A little genuine panic would be highly appropriate. Following every frank assessment of current trends or future catastrophe with optimistic appeals to what might still be possible is self-defeating. We need to say what is true: at the *very* least, if we keep going as we are—and there is absolutely no sign we will succeed in changing that—"*we're not going to make it.*" I.e., there's no reason to think we *are* going to make it.

When we talk sanguinely about the problems the Earth faces, we may get people's attention, but not usually their action. They recognize we are not serious when we condemn the mad consumption of modern life at some rally or meeting and then drive away in our own—perhaps slightly smaller—S.U.V. to our "modest" four-bedroom, three-bath, double-car-garage home located forty miles from our place of employment.

There is, apparently, no need to really take seriously anything we environmentalists say. So no one does. *And neither do we.* Until we begin to take ourselves seriously, environmentalists will *always* remain a fringe element.

The only way out of the mess we're making of this planet is through concerted, worldwide, cooperative effort.[19] Hence, it is impossible to avoid crying out—*truly* crying out. If we are to stand a chance of success, others must unite with us. To get their help, we have to understand and believe in the peril ourselves. But we mustn't let panic overwhelm us. There is time and means to respond to the threat I have foreseen—perhaps not in the way we'd all prefer—but well enough for Life to survive.

---

[19]I'll make the case for a global approach in a few pages.

First we must admit to it, though. Hope doesn't lie in the self-delusion that more of the same, done better, will save us. If we continue acting as if it's no big deal then *no one* is going to regard it as a big deal. If we continue to fight the tide in exactly the same way as we have been, we're done for. *All* of us. Every living thing on Earth. We must begin by recognizing what we've been doing is not working. We are being dragged out to sea. Before we are too tired to save ourselves, we must adopt a new strategy. *Now!*

On How Rationing Works

What the environmental movement is lacking is the motivation that comes with recognizing exactly how dire our situation is. Let me elaborate by telling a little story: I'm an inveterate cross-country hiker. When I go meandering, I prefer to avoid people. So I avoid trails. On four occasions, this preference has resulted in my being unexpectedly caught in the wild overnight. Only once was water a problem.

In the summer of 2001, I'd made plans to share my passion for cross-country traipsing with Pann, an old friend from college. We started up a steep hillside, both hitting our water supply pretty regularly in the warm August temperatures; We weren't worried about water because we expected to spend the night at a creek on the other side of the ridge, which wasn't more than three or four miles. By mid-afternoon, we'd gained about 2500 feet in elevation, which put us very near the 8900 foot level, when Pann, who lives near sea level, suddenly said, "I can't go any further."

He is an avid bicyclist in excellent condition, so I was surprised.

"You kidding?" I asked.

"No, I've got to stop." He began getting out of his pack.

"Okay, let's take a break," I agreed.

"No, I mean I can't go any further today." He was clearly struggling as he wrestled his sleeping bag from the pack.

We were on a slope of maybe forty degrees and I thought I could see the top of the ridge, finally, about 300 feet above us. We'd been looking for it for at least two hours and I was really beginning to feel good about the slope's apparent leveling trend just ahead. I knew sleeping where we were would be difficult, at best, but no amount of reasoning with him could muster enough energy to gain another foot of elevation that day. Altitude sickness is a serious problem for those who come to the high elevations and attempt vigorous activity like this, but this was the first time I'd seen it up close. By offering to move his gear, I finally talked him into repositioning downslope about fifty yards where the ground was more level. He was asleep within moments of our relocating.

The rest of the afternoon and evening until dark I scoured the topo map, double checked our location by triangulation as well as I could with my compass, given the limited field of view I had from the side of a hill in a forest, and pondered our situation. We had few supplies, as it was to be, at most, only an overnight. Left between us was one grapefruit, two energy bars, and only about a pint of water. There was no signal for the cell phone.

Water was the real problem. We had counted on getting to the creek before nightfall, an easy goal, or so we'd thought. I was thirsty.

Whether Pann would be any better in the morning was iffy, at best. If not, he couldn't make the distance to the creek. I wished we'd gone easier on the

water on the way up that hill. Going back the way we'd
come was also too long, and besides, we knew there was
no water in that direction. The Tahoe Rim Trail was not
far off our scheduled path and cutting down it to
Highway 89 was clearly our best plan, but I knew
nothing about the reliability of any of the water sources
we would encounter that way. I was really wanting that
big gulp I usually indulge in at the end of a long period
of exercising. Once we got to the trail, though, we
should be O.K. since we'd be able to bum water from
other hikers.

If Pann could make it to the trail.

If he couldn't, I'd have to hike out on my own
and get help. No other option. If that's how it went,
he'd need all the water we had left.

I was *very* thirsty.

Too f-wording bad. If Pann wasn't better in the
morning, he was in real danger of dying of thirst, for
there was no way of knowing when rescue would get to
him.

There's a scene in the great classic movie, *The
Treasure of the Sierra Madre*[20], starring Humphrey
Bogart, in which a group of miners run out of water. I'd
never been *really* thirsty before in the absence of the
ability to take a drink, and that scene came vividly to my
mind innumerable times that night. I know how they
felt. It's a bit of a stretch, for we weren't lost or
anything, and I would certainly be able to reach water in
the morning, whether he could or not, but I couldn't help

---

[20]*The Treasure of the Sierra Madre*,
Directed by John Huston, Warner Brothers
Pictures, 1948

thinking that it was a very good thing for Pann that we're such good friends. Real thirst is ugly.

I slept very fitfully, and twice wet my lips from the canteen despite myself. At the first sign of light I roused Pann and we discussed our options. He wanted to try to walk out, even though he wasn't feeling much better. We ate the grapefruit like an orange, being sure not to lose any of its moisture, and set off in the predawn light. I wanted to get as much distance under our belts as possible before it got warm. It was about 5:00 a.m.

Pann became my hero that day. He set the pace, and it was *incredibly* slow. I never saw him take a step greater than the length of his foot, and each clearly was a maximal effort. But he must have taken a million of them. Incredible stamina, given his condition. Incredible resolve. We plodded along, finally reaching water at about 1:00 pm, and, although I was desperate for a drink, it hadn't killed me (nor I him). There was even a little water still left in our canteen, and Pann had received sufficient liquid to keep going that whole time. He continued on, in fact, to the highway, as it was all downhill by then, so he walked himself out of a very bad situation.

There are several important lessons here. One is this: *Nothing* stimulates rationing like the realization that you're going to need every bit of what you have left and the fear that even that may not be enough. My potential of dehydration was not really a life-threatening problem, but Pann's most certainly was, even though he probably never got particularly thirsty that day. We were lucky. One more bad turn could have changed that very drastically, so I was motivated to ration the water, and I've never consumed less in a comparable period of time, I assure you. What water we had left was Pann's.

When environmentalists are confronted with a movement whose first premise is nothing short of, "It's *already* too late to save Earth," they will, perhaps, at last be forced to recognize that *real* environmental decline, like real thirst, is going to be ugly. Genocides are not accidental. Nor will they be uncommon.

Whether or not environmentalists agree with its inevitability, hearing the panic in the voices of people who've visualized the ultimate consequence of our species' "success," should serve as a wake-up call. If they recognize the world-wide trends they've been monitoring for years, perhaps the shock of our cry will move environmentalists to finally get serious. As it is now, they haven't fully considered the consequences of not succeeding. If they had, they'd know that we're going to need every resource we have left, and even those may not be enough. Even by their own, more optimistic, view.

If environmentalists ever do learn to take themselves seriously, the movement will get a jolt of energy it's never seen before. I predict it will take wings. Waste will be a thing of the past, for peer pressure will bring it to a halt. Our continual disregard of other creatures, and of the Earth itself, will, finally, cease to be tolerated. Many of our resources might even be treated with a respect which would elevate them to the level of true renewability.

Hope is essential, and the Message certainly had some. But to realize it, we have to first come to *believe* in the danger we are in. The basis of our conservation efforts must move away from the underlying assumption, currently almost universally held, that we don't really need all that natural stuff: it would be nice to keep it, of course, be we can do without it.

Bullshit.

The Cold, Hard Facts

Even many who realize that humans are *the* threat to the planet still fail to recognize this depth of the problem. Yet the record attests to our ineffectiveness at repairing and controlling the damage we've already inflicted. Comparison of the global present to the global past–of *any* period–demonstrates it: we are *not* reversing, or even significantly slowing, the destruction of our planet. Since at least the industrial revolution, we've seen nothing but decline in the ecosystem. And Homo sapiens' success is the cause. **We are a species out of control.**

Anyone who can't recognize that is simply in denial, and those who think manning the bilge pumps is going to keep us afloat forever–or even for a few thousand years–need to take stock of whether they really think they have made progress since they first began trying to heave water overboard. In the overall picture, we've steadily, consistently, and uniformly *lost* ground.

If environmental advocacy groups want to claim victories, they are reduced to pointing out improvements in Los Angeles' smog and successful stopgap measures to preserve bits of habitat while the darkening cloud of global warming gathers on the horizon and the human population mindlessly continues to explode. Sure, we've *slowed* the rate of growth (sometimes and in some places), but–helloooo–the human population is *still* growing. And it's *already too big*. When our definitions of "progress" are all couched in terms of *slowing* our rates of loss, we're not talking about progress at all. We're talking self-deception.[21]

---

[21]It is, perhaps, too harsh, though, to blame environmental leaders and scientists who

No one–*no one*–thinks the Earth is more
receptive to life now than it was before the invention of
agriculture, except, maybe, to humans. No one who
thinks about it and has a true I.Q. greater than 80
believes that we have made real global progress in the
past 2000 years, or 200, or 20, or two. Or one.
Any progress this month?
Noooooope. Not this month. Sorry.
But, "Wait," you say. "There are a number of
scientists who deny that things are this bad and their
I.Q.'s aren't sub-eighty."
Yes, there are. And no, their I.Q.'s aren't below
80. So how do I explain myself?
Well, there's one subgroup of these people who
simply don't get my point at all. It is important that you,
the reader, see their error: it's in the phrase "except to
humans." Many people, including scientists with very
high I.Q.'s, cannot divorce themselves from the totally
erroneous feeling that the only thing that matters is
whether the environment is (i.e., appears to be) more
friendly to human beings. I've inserted "appears to be"
parenthetically there because I want to contrast as starkly
as possible the way this group would make the statement
and the way I would. Mine is the very best this idea
could ever be.

---

have adopted the habit of claiming progress
when they mean only that they are (sometimes)
slowing the rate of decline. It *is* better than
nothing, and it is a first step. But it is also not
"progress." It is slowing the rate of decline.
They are not the same things, and it is too late
for us to continue to indulge the fantasy that
they are.

There is a widely held, but totally pernicious, school of thought that man will be able to survive forever on an ecology populated solely by himself and his domesticated creatures. It's not clear whether people raised in cities, never seeing a forest or jungle, are more susceptible to the fiction that nature is a luxury than are those reared in environments where natural competitors are still a daily threat to individual survival. The former may not see a need for nature at all. The latter tend to be too close to the fight to see mutual trade offs for the overall system. The idea that nature is somehow optional, however, is simply wrong. I will speak to this in more depth later, but it is crucial to keep it in mind throughout this narrative. There is *no* sustainable future for human beings in a world solely of his design. He ain't that f-wording smart or powerful. Never will be.

Self-delusion might explain some legitimate professionals' lack of recognition of the truth, for everyone is immersed in our human-centric culture and we all wish things were better than they are, but anyone who cannot see the environment's direction and the consequences is only fooling himself. Meanwhile, entrenched institutions, interested solely in their own agendas, eagerly exploit the unfortunate innocence of the scientists who are thusly deluded by quoting them liberally and often out of context.

In addition, there's another factor at play here. One subset of the scientific community, not necessarily totally distinct, sees only the good living that's to be made by well-placed intellectuals willing to stand up for the various pressure groups preferring to ignore environmental problems altogether. Their deficit isn't in intelligence, it's in ethics. One ought not be surprised by their presence: *every* profession is liberally seasoned with representatives of the oldest of all professions.

Don't let yourself be fooled any longer. In point of obvious fact, the *rate* of decline in the total biosphere has only increased over time. Distinguishing the mouthpieces and their "Environmental Destruction Lobby" (EDL) sponsors isn't that difficult: their opinions are usually more strident than those legitimate professionals who just can't free themselves from our historical mind-set. But both subgroups are at the root of our decline. Recognize them for what they are and, most importantly of all, challenge and expose them.

Gaia vs. "The Rapture"

Despite my conviction that we humans are bringing this on ourselves, nothing in the Message indicates humans would be the *cause*. The lack of any indication of what, specifically, kills the Earth was striking. But that's not exactly what I'm referring to here. It was crucial to understanding the Vision that humans played no part in it *at all*. There was, quite literally, no mention of Homo sapiens. The "we" in *"We're not going to make it. We've got to get off."* clearly referenced all living entities on this planet, not merely humans. In fact, it was so emphatically inclusive of all Earth-life that it implied "we" are precisely as one: Like the "we" we'd use when speaking of our nuclear family in reference to an unjustified and unexpected eviction notice from the state. We're all in this together. Every living being.

There is an elegant idea that's been around since the 70's in which the Earth itself is viewed as a Lifeform. It has pertinence here. It's called the Gaia Hypothesis, and, when appealing to it, I will call Earth, the living being, "Gaia." The model, originally posed as an attempt to better understand the biological dynamics of our global ecosystem, has evolved in many people's thinking to a level much more mystical and broader in scope. I think it presents a far better visualization of our role in the Lifeforce than any of the old philosophical models, including all current religions with which I am familiar.

Almost five hundred years after Copernicus' realization that Earth is not the center of the universe, our philosophical foundations are still firmly invested in precisely the opposite assumption. At first that seems astounding, for the vehement reaction from the Catholic Church illuminated quite well how clearly Copernicus' observation ran counter to the basic beliefs of the time about the nature of the universe.

Intellectually and scientifically, most of us now pay lip service to the virtual certainty of Life as a universe-wide phenomenon. "We've not discovered it yet, but surely it's out there." Yet that is not how we actually think at all.

We use "universe" in two distinct, diametrically opposed, ways. The most common usage is exemplified in phrases such as "ideas that shook the universe," or "universal health care," neither of which has anything to do with anything beyond the human experience. The other, and the one I wish to address here, references the whole of physical reality, including distant stars, galaxies, nebulae, quasars, and whatever else lies out there.

Imagine viewing Earth from outside our galaxy, the Milky Way. That is, after all, where one would find oneself if randomly placed in the universe to which I'm alluding. From that perspective, one cannot even distinguish the sun, let alone the lightless planets that orbit it. In my usage of the word "universe," the whole of human experience cannot even be located. This is the universe physicists and priests alike are attempting to explain. And, knowingly or not, it is also the universe you and I are talking about when we wonder "what's it all about."

Trouble is, we can't even begin to get a grasp on something that large. Professional scientists may talk about this kind of "universe," but, even for them, it's little more than an intellectual exercise. "Our universe" is, perforce, bounded by *our* experience. Abstractions are, in the final analysis, totally irrelevant to us. Our universe has to do with our day-to-day lives. Had the Church realized this in Copernicus' day, they'd probably have just let the whole thing blow over. But it hardly seems to have mattered. When people do not understand something in the world around them they turn to their faith for answers.

Faith has more to do with our perceptions of *our* universe than does science. In that sense, the Pope and his ideas of reality are far more important than Copernicus and his mathematical view of how the stars work. We have not yet grasped, at anything approaching a truly philosophical level, that the universe not only does not revolve around us or this planet, but that it is as oblivious of us as the ocean is of a snail in one of its tidepools.

A first step toward that kind of understanding of the universe and its scope is to recognize that "we" are Gaia. There is no "we" without Gaia.

Yet the absence of a specific mention of humans in the Vision didn't mean that Homo sapiens will not play a role in the events that will be fatal to Gaia Herself. Whether we do or don't simply wasn't part of the "mind dump." So you should be made aware of the fact that it is only I asserting that human activity will definitely be the trigger. A number of perfectly reasonable alternative scenarios not involving man might have the same result–a major asteroid impact, for example. Most people who talk about such an impact, though, clearly do not view it as a threat to the entire biosphere. It would be a very rare meteor indeed that could destroy all life. Such objects certainly exist, however, and we cannot be certain that one isn't out there, aimed at us, and just not yet discovered. Much smaller asteroids would do the job of killing off humans, and that, by most people's reckoning, would be bad enough. But it's precisely this myopic view that sees humanity as the central question of every issue that we must alter if we are to recognize the nature of the disaster that awaits us and respond. We must begin to recognize our subservience to the greater entity, Gaia.

Our purblindness manifests itself whenever we imagine "end of the world" scenarios only in terms of the human population. We apparently don't relate well to the concept of threats to Gaia itself. We almost never think about the end of the world, only the end of *us*. The "Rapture," for example, is as much about the start of a new phase in our (human's) "eternal life" as it is about the end of this one. No, more: it is a *purely* religious idea. It's not about the world at all. It's about *us*.

We must begin to think beyond all that. This is *not* just about us humans, and it's important to recognize how truly radical this point still is, despite the five hundred years since Copernicus. When I speak of our dying, "we" means every living species with which we can identify, both plant and animal. I'm talking of the death of Gaia. It makes no difference *whatsoever* who or what causes it. Real tragedy trivializes blame.

Even harder for many people to comprehend, is this: *nothing we can do* will save the Earth. On that point the Vision was unequivocally clear. The problems are no longer soluble. Not here. Not on Earth.

It's too late. *"We're not going to make it."*

I can't prove that in any irrefutable way, but neither have I been able to disprove it during all the intervening years. But here, too, the Gaia Hypothesis throws light on our situation. Gaia is not the Earth. It is the Lifeforce that currently resides on Earth. Gaia is to the Earth as the soul is to the body. While there is no longer hope for Earth, yet may Gaia still be saved.

The real downfall for Earth, if it comes through human indifference, will be through our reluctance–even inability–to inconvenience ourselves. We will not respond to the Message that what we are doing–what we *are*–is killing the planet. Clearly, any effective response would require sacrifice on our part. Individuals might do that. Some, even many, obviously will, but not the species as a whole. We have been trained, for centuries, to disregard the Lifeforce itself in deference to our own human needs, and, worse, our wants. We routinely regard the part as much more important than the whole. After all, God made the world *for us*, not for any other creature, or even the whole of the other creatures/beings. We are special/dominant/–*apart*. We alone are endowed with souls.[22] When the world ends, it will be all about *us*, about *our* being raptured up into Heaven to sit by Christ's side.

Or some other such delusion.

---

[22]In fairness, I must admit that I don't know enough about Buddhism, Hinduism, or many other religions to make such a sweeping statement. Maybe there are exceptions. But, if there are, I don't see their influence as so widespread as to stop any of the ill effects that the cultures I *am* familiar with are having.

Delusions that stop so many from even recognizing the danger to Gaia we humans have become. Delusions that make it *possible* for us humans to be so arrogant as to think our disappearance would be such a great loss. It's an attitude that blinds us to the monstrousness of this tragedy we're hurtling toward. We accelerate the plunge to oblivion every day of our lives, every one of us, and especially those of us from the industrialized nations. Americans are far worse than anyone else, in fact. Most of us take 2000+ pounds of metal with us everywhere we travel. We pump heat, created solely for the purpose, into the already hot summer air so we won't have to sweat (that *is* how air conditioning works, you know). Daily, humans burn millions of gallons of oil shipping food thousands of miles across the face of the Earth simply so our palates won't get bored. We contribute every day in a thousand ways, solely for our own vain pleasure and comfort.

But, despite the fact that it will likely be a natural consequence of human excess, it will not be *because* of us that the world is going to end: nothing *we* have done is being punished or rewarded. It's not about God coming down to redeem His/Her/Its *people*, or to punish *us* in some way. This is simply physics: we burn too much oil, we've added too many CFC's, or–who knows what it is, exactly.

It's nothing personal, that's all. It's not some sort of purposeful chastisement or honor from an all-seeing, all-knowing, higher presence. We're not, and never have been, that special. It's just not so. And it's not likely to end with a bolt of blinding light from heaven (the asteroid impact scenario). It looks like it's going to go out hot, dry, and dirty–more like a smoldering campfire than a visitation by some Messiah.

We have never been a specific beneficiary of God's rewards, because it is not *about* us. Of course we've received rewards unnumbered by having been given the gift of being a part of Gaia, this Paradise of a living planet. But so has every other creature, plant and animal, that lives here. It's *Paradise*, for God's sake. Paradise for squirrels and birds and, especially, insects and aquatic Lifeforms. It's *not* solely about people.

We are tiny specks of life in a film of it covering a small rock circling an ordinary star in a galaxy of billions of stars amongst an uncountable multitude of galaxies. Perhaps the Earth can be said to be about the life that inhabits it. I hope so. But the idea that the universe is about humans is *totally* absurd. It's hardly about us at all. Sorry.

That *any* of us believes it is about us, knowing as much about the universe as we do today, is merely proof of our unparalleled conceit. Admittedly, that belief served us well in our rise through the melee that life on Earth has always been, but now it is the core at the center of the threat to all life on this planet.

The reality, however, is that almost all of us think "it," whatever that is, *is* about people. That there might be a large portion of us who really *don't* believe the universe is about human beings, such as the scientific community, for example, is a myth running directly counter to everything about modern culture. The belief in a human-centric universe is a vestige of philosophies rooted in a past during which we were searching for explanations of phenomena that we had no tools to decipher. But it is a myth which is alive and well still, even within the scientific community. That so few scientists ascribe to the Gaia Hypothesis, and so many to religions contrived in antiquity, is all the evidence we need.

That's how the Message was given me. It *is* all about us when you mean "us" to refer to the collective of living beings. On the scale of our present understanding of the universe, it may even be about the "us" that means Gaians. But when you mean "humans," you've got it all wrong. Fatally wrong. For that thinking is *exactly* how we got here and exactly what keeps us on the path to our own ultimate destruction, for when all Life dies, so, obviously, do we.

Damn it! I find myself trapped here in a web of my own weaving. When I began writing this book, I promised myself I would avoid any temptations to present what happened to me that day in Holland as fiction, or to hedge on the Vision by softening it's Message to some sort of warning alerting us to the need to change our ways. There have been *very* strong temptations to do both and the only way I've resisted is by rigorously adhering to a policy of *absolute* honesty. By that rule I have to admit that I've just caught myself in a logical error which I must now explain and, simultaneously, somehow defend:

Gödel

There is a well-known fact from mathematics called "Gödel's Theorem." It speaks to assumptions and the kinds of mathematical systems to which they lead. Man is, basically, a logical creature, and Gödel's Theorem has deep implications for philosophy, cosmology, and religion–probably for any subject which attempts, even in the slightest, to apply reason to understand reality.

Every logical system must begin by accepting certain words or expressions as so basic that they cannot be defined–one simply assumes a common understanding. To see why that is necessary, consider: if you were to define a line as being a geometric object having only one dimension, then you need a definition for "dimension." If that involves the concept of "direction," then, of course, you would need to define that. Eventually one needs to simply stop defining the terms used in definitions, lest one starts going in circles.

Similar kinds of thinking reveals the necessity of formulating some properties that are simply assumed to be true. Any parent who has, finally, decided to simply answer "just because" to a child's repeated inquiry of "why?" knows the necessity of these practices. So, once the undefined terms are posited, a basic set of assumptions about them must be agreed to; assumptions which are *not* to be "proven." They are the starting points. These are the axioms of the system.

Although it may not be so well thought out or structured, everyone in the world has their own personal sets of undefined terms and axioms. Without them you simply can't have a belief system, and we all have a number of those. "Everyday man's" axioms usually answer questions like, "Is there a God?" "Is there only one, and if so, is He a he, She a she, or It only an it?" and "What's He/She/It like?" Some questions, such as "Does man have free will,"[23] may be answered by either making a basic assumption or by drawing conclusions from basic assumptions. If the latter, then a mathematician would call the conclusion a theorem.

From their axioms, mathematicians prove theorems using logical rules which are essentially the

---

[23]I.e., is he able to determine his/her own fate? See, e.g., http://en.wikipedia.org/Free_will

same as those most people ascribe to in their own lives. Likewise, in real life, people's bottom line beliefs (the axioms) and undefined terms lead to belief systems such as Religions, cults, cultures, or political philosophies. "Everyman" is not nearly so devoted to logical rules and details as mathematicians are, so I'm stretching the analogy greatly, but I think it will prove instructive nonetheless.

I'll just refer to "Everyman's" theorems as "answers to questions," with the understanding that the answers may be in various states of agreement as to whether or not, and how many, people accept them. Basic assumptions, then, are "axioms." Conclusions, even loosely derived from these assumptions, are "answers to questions" and are equivalent, for our purposes, to the mathematical concept of "theorems."

In the mathematician's world, there are two distinct, *un*desirable kinds of systems. The first is one in which there are questions which cannot be answered. Such a system is said to be "incomplete." The second is a system in which it is possible to answer some questions one way using some of the axioms, and just the opposite way using others. That type is called "inconsistent."

In the early twentieth century, one of the main occupations of mathematics was an attempt to develop a system which was neither inconsistent nor incomplete. But Kurt Gödel, a logician and close friend of Albert Einstein, put that effort to rest in 1934 when he proved it is impossible to create a meaningful logical system which is both complete *and* consistent. Any logical system *must* be undesirable in the one way, the other, or both. If you try to answer every question there is (i.e., be complete), you *have to* make assumptions which are, at their heart, contradictory (i.e., be inconsistent).

Completeness implies inconsistency. Or, put the other way around: consistency implies incompleteness.

If not being able to answer questions is so intolerable to you that you accept enough axioms to provide an answer to every question, then you will find yourself with some questions that you are sure of the answer one way today, and the opposite way tomorrow. Many such questions, I'm sure. In this case, you find yourself with a set of "rules," each of which has numerous exceptions.

If, on the other hand, consistency is what you most value in a belief system, there will be a large set of questions which are simply beyond your ability to answer. And you won't have the comfort of going to an authority, such as the clergy, a professor, or Mom, for directions as to how to respond to a lot of your dilemmas, since their logic, no matter how inspired, is as bound by Gödel's result as yours.

If you want all the answers, expect a lot of them to contradict one another. If you can't abide contradictions, then you must learn to tolerate ambiguity, because not every question will have an answer. But you can't have it both ways.

Living With Gödel

Most ordinary people seem to prefer completeness over consistency. I think they are unaware of this tendency, for no one seems to recognize their own inconsistencies. Providing the answers to every one of life's many big questions is the main function of every religion. I'm not aware of any culture (other than mathematics) which opts for a consistent system over a complete one.[24]

People simply ignore any contradictions that arise from their belief systems: love thy neighbor, forgive them, and turn the other cheek. All hand in hand with racism, " an eye for an eye," and "preventative" war. On the other hand, every question from, "Is there a heaven?" to "How many angels can dance on the head of a pin?" seems to have not just one, but numerous answers readily ascribed to by millions. Agnostics seem to be rare; theists whose gods have elaborate sets of intricate instructions, the rule.

Even agnostics appear to be comfortable with contradictions in their belief systems. Agnostics and rationalists alike often pride themselves on their decision not to jump to any unwarranted religious conclusions, yet fall victim to the seduction of seeking answers. Many boast about their belief that God, if He/She/It exists at all, certainly does not notice or concern Him/Her/Itself with humans. And yet "knowing" that God *doesn't* do something is as much an answer to the implied question as is "knowing" that He/She/It *does*. Similarly, atheists are just as surely failing in their certitude as the most devout followers of any messiah.

A negative answer is no less an answer than is a positive one. And it is here that my own logic has just been coming up short: While it is obvious that our

---

[24]It must be acknowledged, however, that this description applies only to the mathematicians' professional activities. When it comes to our personal lives and moral beliefs, we are just as apt to be inconsistent as anyone else.

assumption that "it" is about "us" (humans) has led us to the verge of the destruction of Gaia, I cannot really claim to *know* that "it" *isn't* about "us." The question is itself clearly one which presupposes so much to get an answer as to make contradictions unavoidable. All I can say, for sure, is that the destruction of Gaia, which would obviously include our own destruction, is too high a price to pay for making the assumption that "it *is* about us" an axiom, as so many currently do.

That's all I'm really trying to say: we *have* to stop acting as if "It's all about us" is obvious. Couching it in terms of "it's *not* all about us," however, is overreaching. My defense: we're so used to thinking the way we do that the only way to make it clear that I *don't* believe "It's about us," is to claim I *believe* "It's not about us." Truth is, I just don't think *any*one knows, or *can* know.

But whether "it" is, or isn't, is not the point. Our *assumption* that it is, blinds us to the horror of our destruction of Gaia, and, thereby makes that destruction tolerable to us. This, apparently, despite our utter inclusion as a part of that which we destroy.

Why Not Just Let Nature Run its Course?

On this small rock, circling our ordinary star in this little nook of the universe, we humans have succeeded so well as a species that nothing can stop us now from killing the planet. Like a cancer, humans have grown to the point of consuming the host.

Like cancer cells, there are simply too many of us. Overpopulation is the essence of the problem, and we will never voluntarily reduce our population. The fleeting existence of the "zero population growth" (ZPG) movement in the post-sixties era seemed hopeful, at first, but it failed profoundly. Now, after decades of watching the population problem only grow worse, the almost complete absence of ZPG from today's popular discussions verifies our inability to restrain ourselves.

Sadly, the only "successful" efforts at reducing population seem to involve defining an "us" and a "them," breeding hatred for "them," and then conducting mass genocide, as in Nazi Germany, Cambodia, Rwanda, Bosnia, or Darfur. Of course, the goal of population control wasn't explicitly appealed to in any of these examples: but why appeal to that when the more obvious motives of competition for wealth, in any of its elemental forms (water, land, food, sanitation, money, health care, etc.) are more acceptable drivers of hatred?

Alternatively and more passively, but all the more effective for it, control of "their" population may be effected by simply failing to respond adequately to crises affecting "them," such as is being done today in all of Africa with regard to the AIDS epidemic.

These and similar methods, though, are both onerous on the short-term and doomed as real solutions in the long. They rely on ever narrower definitions of an acceptable "us" which itself simply continues to grow. Changing the players in no way addresses the problem of there being increasingly too many players.

Pointing to China as a counterexample to the suggestion that we can't control our urge to propagate, as some like to do, is nothing more than another example of our mistaking the cutting of loses for the very different phenomenon of making progress.[25] The

---

[25]It should be mentioned, as well, that China's much vaunted "one child" policy is beginning to show signs of eroding, and may

population problem is like the Dough boy: poke it here and see it swell elsewhere. Every China is counterbalanced by an India, or Indonesia, or Mexico. The world's population is the issue and the *rate* of growth is not the problem, it is the very *fact* of the growth. Only negative worldwide growth would reverse our impact on Gaia.

The Vision (3): Destination?

Some people do realize the horrific size of the threat to our ecosystem that we humans represent and are willing to consider something as drastic as getting off the planet "as insurance."[26] They are, however, not a very vocal group. Most of them, it seems, are either intimidated by the relatively slim promise of space travel or simply assume space will be a natural extension of human existence.

The latter group appears to be content to wait, not sensing any urgency. The former usually just throws up its hands in frustration at the innumerable obstacles current affairs place in the way of any serious efforts to overcome the challenges of space exploration and development.

---

soon be viewed more as an example of failed good intentions than an ultimate success story.

[26]As of this writing, press reports indicate the famous physicist, Stephen Hawking, has just publicly asserted precisely this position. It remains to be seen if his profile will be high enough to encourage others to "come out of the closet."

The Vision's second statement, *"We've got to get off"* so clearly meant "get off the planet," that I have never known for sure whether the rest of what transpired immediately following it was a part of the Message or not. Because of that uncertainty, I have withheld it until now. Immediately following this line, the voice changed to something much more like my own internal voice and said, *"We've got to go to Mars."*

That peculiar change in voice has been *very* hard for me to analyze. Complicating the issue is the fact that the idea itself is tainted in a number of other ways as well. Besides its "add-on" feel, it was also the only portion of the entire experience that was directed at humans. Surely, a "we" having the scope I've been discussing wouldn't necessarily require relocation to Mars to outlive the Earth. For example, cold-tolerant aquatic algae might be able to survive in the ice-covered oceans of Europa, one of Jupiter's moons. If so, all we'd need is a means of safely delivering live algae to that environment. In addition, the discovery in the last few years of a wide variety of extremophiles[27] on Earth suggests that this broader definition of "we" would certainly invite more possibilities than a simple conclusion that Mars must be "our" destination.[28]

---

[27]Lifeforms adapted to environments extremely hostile to most other types of Lifeforms, for example, hot springs, or high aquatic pressures, acidic or caustic conditions, etc.

[28]At this writing, exciting news is coming in of the potential discovery of an altogether unexpected phenomenon in the solar

Consequently, I'm not sure whether that last sentence, *"We've got to go to Mars,"* was truly a part of the Message or not. On the one hand, I still felt very much in the throes of the Vision, but on the other, I may have been reaching a conclusion on my own rather than passively receiving something being handed me along with the rest.

However, if we are to expect the enthusiasm of Homo sapiens for this venture, we'll need a venue which includes hope for our (small meaning) own survival. According to my research since the Vision, Mars offers the only possibility for that. Therefore, divinely inspired or not, I will now confine most of my remarks to this question: How do we get to Mars?

At first, the entire idea of getting off the planet to Mars, or anywhere else, as a means of addressing the problems we face here on Earth may sound utterly ridiculous, but please hear me out because now I begin the most important task set me. Having gone to some length to convince you that my Vision of an impending, unavoidable, death of the planet Earth is plausible, I must now convince you of something seemingly even more absurd: that interplanetary colonization is not only a viable chance for survival, it is our *only* chance if we intend that survival to include human beings. Furthermore, to fulfill my Mission, I must convince you to work toward a goal which you cannot attain in your lifetime, for our task is one for generations. Not you,

---

system: another locale, Enceladus, a Saturnian moon, where liquid water may be abundant. This would make these comments even more valid.

nor I–nor any of our children–will see the end of this endeavor.

Neither can I pretend to be working on avoiding the "impending end of the Earth." I repeat: it will not be saved. Clear and certain. It will be a dead planet, revolving and rotating still, presumably, but utterly lifeless.

We can begin the Mission, however. And nothing in the Vision implied that we cannot postpone the end of Life on Earth. If we are to succeed in getting off, in fact, we *must* slow the rate of its demise. As I shall show in the next section, we must also start the project of getting off now, otherwise the ultimate failure is guaranteed.

In one sense, though, if it were really only about us humans–if we were the only, or even the primary victims to suffer at the death of Gaia–I would agree with the large number of people who, on hearing my story of the Vision, simply say, "let nature run its course." But they are, I think, misinterpreting the Vision. It's *all* of Earth-kind that dies. I tend to agree that a creature as iniquitous as the human doesn't deserve to survive to the end of time. It should have been us who went extinct long ago, not the Dodo, nor the Passenger Pigeon, nor any of those species that continue to go extinct every hour of every day.[29] The Dodo was trusting. We are arrogant. The Dodo could never have destroyed the Earth.

We can. And will.

Advocates of the "let nature run its course" school seem to underestimate the potential for

---

[29]Most estimates range between two and five each hour.

destruction of our current campaign against Gaia. I suspect that, although, the potential of our (humans) destroying ourselves may not seem so horrible to them, if they truly recognized the possibility of our destroying *all* Life on Earth, they would abandon their position instantly, for such people tend to be the least malevolent I know. Whether or not the extinction of Homo sapiens seems natural and deserving to you, what possible harm have dolphins done? Or trees? Or nematodes? Why should *they* be denied a future because of man's mistakes? That is only a small fraction of the damage we inflict now if we don't intervene. Letting nature "run its course" is merely another variant of human self-centeredness—"*we* screwed up–royally–so all of you can just perish with us." But this attitude can only survive if it coexists with denial of the reality of the horror we are perpetrating.

The "Open Window" Space Myth
vs. Space Fact

Perhaps the most startling aspect of the Vision was its insistence that, *"We've got to get off."* That confounds people like few other aspects of my Message, especially when I start talking about Mars as a destination. Interestingly, I seem to get two opposing reactions when I tell people we *have* to go there, and not infrequently, from the exact same people.

Probably the most common response is one of "all in due time, my lad, all in due time." It is essentially taken for granted that, one day, humans will be a space-faring species, colonizing distant planets, exploring faraway worlds, and going "where no man has gone before."

The other reaction is one of incredulousness at the idea that we can travel to, and inhabit, Mars, especially as any kind of reasonable response to a life crisis on Earth today. Someday in the distant future, sure. But not tomorrow, or next year, or in the next few decades. Probably in the next century, and certainly three or four hundred years down the line. But not as a response to man's current path of Earth annihilation. Get real!

The reality is much more complicated than either of these two responses indicate. Let's start with some of the nuance that "getting into space" actually entails.

There is a wonderful novel by George Stewart, *Earth Abides*,[30] which inadvertently addresses the first, and most glaring, misunderstanding that most people, including many actual rocket scientists, have about man's future in space. The novel follows the life of a man, Ish, who survives a terrible plague which sweeps the Earth, killing something like 599,999 out of every 600,000 people.

The story dramatizes the dependence of technology on a dense population. At first the dominant repercussion for Ish's life is his utter isolation, for water and power systems continue automatically, regulated by machinery which requires little maintenance; Canned and frozen goods, gas, and weapons for hunting feral livestock, etc., are freely available in the empty shops; Surviving immediately beyond the plague is not the problem.

As the plot unfolds over Ish's lifetime, however, the systems fail, the supplies deteriorate with age, and technology drops away until the remaining human population regresses completely to the stone age.

---

[30]Stewart, George R., *Earth Abides*, Random House, New York, N.Y.,1949

The novel convincingly shows that technology is a function of population. This reversion to a primitive lifestyle is both predictable and inevitable. When there are only 100 people in a closed society, *totally* dependent upon themselves for their survival, they do not have toilets. It would not only be absurd because of the lack of necessity for it, it is simply *impossible*. The technology of toilets requires too many people. For one thing, it presupposes a water system. Water systems do not work without plumbing. And plumbing requires pipes, which don't just spring from the ground. Somebody, almost always at a great distance from the application point, manufactures them, usually using metal mined in a separate, even more remote location. Somebody has to deliver them over that great distance. Someone had to build the truck, or wagon, or whatever, and others the road, etc., etc. Knowing how a toilet works is not the issue. The job is just too large unless the population is also large. It requires an infrastructure impossible to support without a minimum population base. One hundred is not enough. Nor is 1000 or 10,000, or, if the society is truly closed, even 100,000.

As with toilets, so also with spaceships. Far more so.

All our favorite heros from our fictionalized future in space, have one thing in common: they have a home planet where industry and advanced technology thrives. The importance of that cannot be overstated. Spaceships, with their populations of (only) thousands, cannot function for long without periodic visits to a home base for resupply and, even more importantly, maintenance. The master engineers of the real future, like Star Trek's Scotty or Jordy, may be amazingly good at getting the most out of their space vessels' miraculous technology, but, without a home planet and its huge population, they'll be unable to process rubber to replace seals, silicone for computer chips, steel to fix that bent I-beam from the last encounter with the real-life equivalent of the Borg, or some other basic ingredient of a crucial component of the ship.

No starship, nor star base, will be able to survive on its own. Not forever. Not ever. Eventually some vital, elemental, part or another will give out, and there will be no replacement or remedy. Getting into space is not, in and of itself, a solution to the problem of long-term survival. "Getting into" is not, in any way, equivalent to "staying."

My point in alluding to a 1940's novel[31] is this: when we lose the home planet, we lose all the space ships and space stations we may have established. Oh, space farers may outlast the home planet for awhile, but without an alternative, habitable planet to support them, they are doomed. Sooner or later, their artificial structures will fail. Therefore we must find and populate an alternative planet. Short of that there is simply no long-term security for Earthlings of any sort.

This is the first and most important lesson about our future in space to understand: *nothing* short of another planet which is hospitable to Earth-based life will suffice. Spaceships and stations are useless. A mere outpost on an inhospitable planet, no matter its size, is nothing but a space station. For us, "going into space" must be a nonsense concept unless its goal is

---

[31]Ironically, this novel, at some levels (including its title), actually reinforces the false perception that Life on Earth will invariably continue no matter what happens to (or because of) man.

"staying in space forever, totally independent of the home planet." "Going" is of no use whatever unless it includes "self-sufficient and self-sustaining."

How The Window
Might Be Opened Further

The vastness of space, however, is prohibitive. It will not do to locate a planet suitable for human habitation some number of light years away: we are incapable of reaching such locales and will remain so for centuries at least. The only practical place for us to look is within the solar system. Unfortunately, since the Apollo missions, we *have* looked, and there are no suitable planets here, not insofar as *already* being habitable, at least. What is possible, however, is taking one of the planets within the solar system and building an ecosystem on it sufficiently Earthlike to allow human habitation.[32] Essentially, the idea is to build and populate an alternative to planet Earth almost entirely from scratch.

I know it sounds preposterous, talking about building an alternative planet, but, in fact, a few scientists are doing exactly that (talking, I mean). Their field is called "Planetary Engineering," and one of their primary creative tasks is to plan the "terraforming" of planets. Terraforming is the process of turning an alien

---

[32]The alert reader will recognize this apparent reversal of my previous de-emphasis of the human role. But remember, we (humans) *will* be required to make the transition possible for any of us (Gaians), and humans don't often do things for altruistic motives alone.

world into something of a duplicate of the Earth, i.e., a place where Earth-originated Lifeforms can survive without artificial life support of any kind. Terraforming involves planet-wide changes on the order of drastic alteration of the chemical composition of the exotic atmosphere, increasing global average ambient temperatures, and bringing forth vast amounts of water from deep underground, sometimes frozen, aquifers.

It is agreed that Mars is the very nearest venue for terraforming. In fact, Mars is really the only place where the idea is currently even remotely possible.

The means of terraforming Mars will likely involve increasing the mass of the Martian atmosphere by releasing base elements from the regolith that will either support Earth Lifeforms or help raise the temperature on the planet, or both. Mars' current mean temperatures range from $^-125°F$ ($^-87°C$) to $^-13°F$ ($^-25°C$) and atmospheric pressure is approximately equal to our atmospheres' pressure at 110,000 ft (33,528 m).[33]

Increasing the mass of atmosphere is necessary because currently Mars cannot even *sustain* liquid water on its surface for long. Temperature is obviously important because otherwise Mars will remain a frozen world in which plant life would be extraordinarily difficult to cultivate.

The next task would be aquafication. If current indications that water may still reside frozen in or even on the surface prove true, this simply means releasing and purifying it. If water is not already available,

---

[33]William K Hartman, *A Traveler's Guide to Mars*, Workman Publishing N.Y., 2003, p 5.

however, the necessary chemicals to actually make water *are* abundant on Mars, and it can be produced, given sufficient energy budgets.

Finally, introduction of viable Lifeforms transplanted from Earth would be necessary. The thinking, essentially, is that the early development of Life on Earth can be mimicked in a very condensed time scale on Mars by judiciously retracing the steps that took billions of years here by periodically introducing the appropriate building blocks artificially.

These are slow processes and it is easier to see how current estimates in excess of 300 years arise than how the more pessimistic sounding upper limit of 900 years might, in fact, even be reasonable.

Planetary engineering is a speciality which has not yet gained much favor, for a number of reasons. The two most discouraging aspects are probably the immensity of the job and the lack of available funding in the field. More the latter than the former, I suspect.

Another discouraging factor is the fact that many people, including a large number of scientists, automatically discount the idea of terraforming Mars without giving it any serious consideration. This is unfortunate for several reasons. If elevated to a high priority, the task is not as quixotic as it first sounds, and therefore deserves more than an automatic discount, especially from scientists.

Moreover, most people reject the idea on the basis of philosophical beliefs deeply held by western culture (at least) rather than careful, rational assessment of the project's practicality. I will extensively discuss this philosophical underpinning and its numerous effects shortly.

Another reason people adopt the "that's absurd" position in response to this idea is that they see no reason to terraform Mars at all. This is where I most emphatically diverge from common thought. I am motivated by a Vision that foretells the death of this planet. I see a *need* to get off this planet that virtually no one else does. Hopefully, after having read this far, you now share some of that sense of need with me.

If you do, there are some things of which you should be aware.

Science as Fiction

Recently, I think I've begun to understand why so many people find terraforming Mars far-fetched. Perhaps the most important factor is that most people alive today have little or no recollection of the race to the Moon. Those too young to remember John F. Kennedy's proposal in 1961 to go to the Moon are simply too young to understand how astounding it was. When I was growing up, "going to the Moon" was used as an idiom for "it's impossible." As soon as Kennedy said, "We're going to do it," that understanding was no longer viable. His challenge was breathtaking.

After about 1975, the manned space program ceased to be the major focus of American scientific activity. The generations which have matured since then have largely developed their understanding of man's mastery of science from "bad science" fiction, i.e., fantasy. The closer to today you come from that date, of course, the worse it gets. *Harry Potter* and *The Lord of the Rings* may be good fiction–good literature, even–but they are *not* a good substitute for true science fiction, which is always rooted in scientific possibility. Sci-fi technology may not exist yet, but it needs to be reasonable to think it might some day. Otherwise it doesn't qualify for the genre. Not so with fantasy. The prevalence of pure fantasy in young people's literature, and worse, popular culture, is now a longstanding tradition.

Don't get me wrong, I'm not saying the young people of today believe the fantasy they grew up on. My point is quite the opposite. They *know* better than to believe it. What I'm saying is that, partly because they *do* know better than to believe it, they don't trust, at a rather deep level, our abilities to accomplish seemingly impossible feats. But, perhaps worse, they also have little concept of *how* to do truly difficult things.

Those of us who saw "going to the Moon" become, not an expression of what humans were incapable of, but rather the exact opposite, have an entirely different perspective on man's future in space than do the younger generations. For us, nothing about "going to the moon" was fictional. We *know* that these things can be accomplished, if only mankind sets its mind to it. But we also know something of how big these tasks can be. It's not a well-practiced flick of the wand. Nor is it something you do by yourself; it takes years of nationally coordinated effort. And more. A real space presence will *not* come about accidently–or even "naturally." It won't just happen: *not in a million years.*

For perhaps 80% or more of the population, going to the moon is their forefathers' mythological story and terraforming another planet is only a modern fantasy. So long as that is all it is in their minds, so shall it remain.

Getting to Mars, in any form, is not a magical fantasy. Just exploring Mars is an immense marshaling and execution of industrial, intellectual and scientific resources and skills. I am proposing a long, hard, and expensive undertaking. To establish so much as a manned station on Mars is a daunting proposition. Terraforming Mars is at least two orders of magnitude more difficult. But it can be done. *That* you need to know. *That* you need to believe.

Make no mistake about it, though, planetary engineering *is* rocket science. It is also philosophy and mathematics and industrial might. Most of all, terraforming Mars will require dedication beyond any given to any task in human history.

Unfortunately, that brings us to another thing planetary engineering is: political science. That it currently garners so little monetary support is indicative of the problem. As I mentioned earlier, planetary engineers offer time estimates for terraforming Mars ranging from 300 years to almost 900, assuming today's technologies and a consistent effort throughout. More recent papers seem to support the smaller estimates and significant advances in the state of the art will, presumably, lower the estimates still more. Historically, however, only a very few governments and a few more religions have even survived long enough to complete the work of terraforming a planet. It is, in fact, hard to conceive of this project succeeding unless it becomes a worldwide effort.

That nine-hundred year clock can't even be started, though, until public support puts the project on the agenda. If my judgment of current public enthusiasm for space programs is correct, such public support won't happen soon, and consistent effort over long periods of time also seems very unlikely. While the scientists who have looked at the idea agree that it is possible, most realists, including many enthusiastic supporters, have little expectation that terraforming Mars will even begin in the first half of the twenty-first century. We will, perhaps, have outposts there by then, but even that depends on a great many unknown variables.

The thrust of the Vision was that Earth may not survive even for three hundred years. The good news, though, is that these terraforming figures are all based on the human-centric idea that the job is not finished until Mars has an environment hospitable to humans. And I concur, but I have *seen* the Earth without life of any kind, and if we can save blue-green algae, we will have done a marvelous thing. Or, more accurately, we will have *un*done a small portion of the most horrific thing imaginable, the extinction of the (Earth-based) Lifeforce.

Even establishing blue-green algae on Mars, however, will be arduous and certainly will mark an important milepost along the way to the eventual construction of an environment satisfactory to humans. As to the question of how long it will take to make Mars hospitable to the so-called "lower" Lifeforms, none of the sources I've looked at seem to care. Certainly it will be less than the 300-900 year estimate based on the ideal of *human* habitation. From my point of view, that is *very* encouraging.

But we would be obtuse in the extreme if we thought humans would even consider working on these problems if they saw nothing in it for themselves. Our moral obligation, as the only species having the ability to do it, may be to preserve the Lifeforce, but there's no way in hell humans will go down the path I've just outlined unless their own survival is a possible outcome. We're not that kind of beast. Fortunately, it *is* conceivable that we might make it to Mars, too. So that's what we must appeal to. We must strive for human procreation to a new planet, not just successful transplantation of blue-green algae. It's how we must regard the task: making survival of *humans* possible. In that sense, and in that sense alone, it *is* about us. That being said, it's also worthy of re-emphasizing that, if humans don't get involved, *nothing* will survive.

So, going to the stars will not be natural, or easy, or magic. It will be hard, require world-wide devotion to the effort, and call for dedication through numerous decades, at least. But there is yet another, and in many ways more pressing, difficulty with the assumption that humans will inevitably go forth into outer space and multiply. And I remind you, according to the Vision, if we don't get at least some species off this planet, Gaia is doomed.

Slamming the
Not-So-Open Window Shut

While it may have been surprising to realize that establishing an independent presence in space is so vast an undertaking as terraforming a planet, what we most urgently need to recognize now is the limited time available to us in which to begin the task.

The manned space program has languished ever since the moon missions and is currently incapable of endeavors beyond Low Earth Orbit (LEO). All current deep space work is done via robotics. Any attempt to repeat the human accomplishments of the 1969-75 era will require vast amounts of investment in infrastructure, essentially re-creating much of that which made going to the moon possible. The expense involved will be huge and corresponding public support will need to be garnered if we ever expect to develop a mission to Mars. But, while the manned extra-orbital program has long since been discontinued, we have been active in LEO, as have numerous other nations, and today there are more than 2000 satellites circling the planet.

Ironically, this continued activity in space, minimal in scope as it has been, now presents us with a legacy which is potentially the greatest impediment to a continued manned space program. The opportunity to become a truly space-faring planet (i.e., beyond LEO), contrary to popular belief, is not an empty, always open, window. It can be, and, in fact, likely will be, slammed tightly shut.

Besides the high monetary cost of space exploration, the occasional tragic cost in lives fosters a deep resistance which frequently threatens our commitment to humans venturing beyond our atmosphere. With both the Challenger and the Columbia Shuttle disasters came loud calls to abandon, if not space altogether, certainly its manned exploration. But this periodical reaction to human costs pales in comparison to one potential "worst case," scenario–a very probable scenario–which demands our attention. I'm not just concerned that some accidental tragedy will put the brakes on our zealousness while we get a better handle on the technology; When I say "slammed tightly shut," I mean "ended forever."

Consider the Space Shuttle Columbia's loss: for a time, the leading theory on Columbia's destruction as it reentered the atmosphere from LEO was that it had struck a piece of space junk. The danger of space junk is well known in the astronautical community. Because of their high relative velocity of thousands of miles per hour, even tiny objects (e.g., button-sized), become lethal projectiles when striking a spacecraft. As satellites have proliferated in LEO, this problem has reached a near-crisis level. As a by-product of placing those 2000+ satellites in orbit, we now also have some 8000 ancillary objects in orbit that could easily bring a spacecraft down. Until this junk is removed from orbit, safe access to space is far from assured, and the problem continues to grow.

A great many of the 2000 satellites in LEO are military and will certainly be targets in the next war between great powers. This would surely mark the end of Earth's space age, for their destruction will be messy. Every targeted satellite will instantly become thousands of shards of shrapnel, forever (essentially) orbiting Earth looking for a space vessel to penetrate. Overnight, the possibility of getting humans into space will be severely limited, if not extinguished altogether. Such a war, even if it doesn't result in the complete breakdown of civil society on the surface of the Earth, would put so much space junk in orbit that we would never be able to send humans into space again.

These considerations imply a potentially severe limitation on our time frame. There is certainly no reason to think such a war is forever avoidable, or even that it won't happen in the next fifty years. In fact, the world has seldom gone fifty years without war, and we've been relatively lucky in seeing the major conflicts since WWII confined to regional theaters.

Even without this horrendous scenario, however, if the problem of space junk is not solved relatively soon, the cost of sending people into space will become prohibitive not just in terms of money, but lives. If we continue to avoid international conflict, I suspect that the gradual accumulation of junk will eventually be addressed. But it is certainly not guaranteed[34].

---

[34]We need a major monetary prize for inventors to create a device which will clear space of junk. This would be an excellent starting point for endowments or individuals

The point is worth repeating: if there is ever an all out war between two nations with orbit-attaining capabilities, military satellites will be amongst the highest priority targets. When that occurs, it marks the end of mankind entering space, for crossing through the resulting rain of deadly space debris will be suicidal. The Earth will be enshrouded in a matter of, at most, days, and humans will be trapped on this planet forever.

If we don't succeed in getting off this planet *soon,* we may not be able to get off at all. So much for the "last frontier."

Because of this risk one of our very highest priorities must be prevention of such a war ever happening. The significance of what I've been saying here should not be overlooked, for, remember, there is no security for Earthlings until we have built an "alternative Earth." Space-based weapons systems and defense satellites are more dangerous to the future of the Lifeforce than any other single current human activity. Nothing short of world peace provides an environment in which we will be able to propagate to other planets.

The Longer We Wait, The Harder It Gets

Another consideration which makes the assumption that our future lies in outer space appear rather Pollyannaish also derives from the observation in

---

with sufficient means to contribute to the salvation of life from this planet. In truth, though, I'm not certain such doesn't already exist, as there have been substantial contributions along this line in recent years (see, for example, http://www.spaceward.org/).

Earth Abides that technology demands a certain population to sustain it. This insight is paralleled and refined by Jared Diamond in *Guns, Germs, and Steel*,[35] an anthropological examination of why some cultures advanced more quickly than others. Diamond makes three good points. The first is that, for a culture to blossom, it needed access to a food source which could be domesticated, and some had advantages in this regard others did not. The second is that the rate at which various cultures developed depended greatly upon whether or not they also were blessed with available, docile large animals. I.e., in addition to a large population with a secure food source, an *excess* of other resources was also crucial. Necessity may be the mother of invention, but an abundance of resources is the father. Agriculture provided the secure source of food, but the societies that succeeded in the competition with others had the additional advantage of oxen (or some other beast of burden) hanging around the farm, just waiting for someone to think of putting them to work pulling a plow. The third point is that populations must reach certain numbers *before* technological advances can take place.

Today, as the human population continues to expand, we have reached a situation in which our natural resources are beginning to diminish. Not just oil, but the supply of fresh water, forests, and arable farmland. While these problems may be *temporarily* addressed by exploiting the sea in ways not yet developed, that vast resource will also be exhausted, and in a surprisingly

---

[35]Diamond, Jared, *Guns Germs and Steel: The Fates of Human Societies*, WW Norton & Co. New York, N.Y., 1997

short time, if we don't learn to stop our growth. Technological advances may also help, but those who think that the oceanic well won't also run dry don't understand the law of exponential growth.

In another recent work, *Collapse: How Societies Choose to Fail or Succeed,*[36] Diamond talks about how and why certain highly developed cultures disappeared. He describes numerous cultures which, at the height of their apparent success, suddenly and/or completely disintegrated. A common theme is the fighting which breaks out when the effects of resource depletion become evident and everyone begins competing for the remaining vital supplies.

We humans are rapidly reaching the time when our resources will be so limited that managing to sustain ourselves will be problematic. Expansion to other worlds is not going to be an option then. Eking out survival on this one will dominate human activity. That Earth's resources are finite is an obvious fact. One need not be a scientist to argue this point. That humans are using those resources up is also obvious.[37] That we are

---

[36]Diamond, Jared, *Collapse: How Societies Choose to Fail or Succeed*, Viking Penguin, New York, N.Y., 2005

[37] There was a famous bet between the late Dr. Julian Simon and Dr. Paul Ehrlich in 1980 which the "Earth Destruction Lobby" (EDL) loves to cite as proof of exactly the opposite. If you've been impressed by the EDL's arguments on this matter, let me refer you to Dr. Ehrlich's comments at http://www.stanford.edu/group/CCB/Pubs/Ecof

in grave danger of trapping ourselves on this planet is, I hope, now apparent. Unless we do something about it soon, we'll be stuck on a toxic, dying planet fighting over the scraps of remaining resources with no hope of escape.

A Reverse Reality Check:
Shouldn't We Worry
About Trashing Another Planet?

There are some in the same school of mea culpa-ists as the "let nature run its course" people who point to humans' annihilative history and worry about how awful it would be if we were to have similar effects on another planet. Their concern seems to be that, if we go to Mars, we will destroy it just like we're destroying Earth.

That's nonsense.

Even if you ignore the fact that we would have apparently started with a barren planet, *already* "destroyed," there are several reasons to abandon this line of thinking. If we succeed in terraforming Mars, all creditable scenarios presume we will have introduced massive numbers of organisms from our planet to effect desired changes in the Martian ecosystem. For example, the initial use of blue-green algae is suggested by its role as a natural transforming agent in the early history of our own atmosphere. For lack of a better name, let's call such Earth-originated, living tools for terraforming a planet "terraforganisms."

Although the first permanent human explorers will probably be dealing with a planet essentially bereft of life, introducing terraforganisms will be an early priority in the effort to morph Mars into a living planet.

---

ablesdocs/thebet.htm

Agriculture and forestation will be utilized as soon as the ecosystem will support them. Years before truly significant numbers of humans are living on Mars these processes will have moved beyond the artificial constraints of enclosures. Martian communities in self-contained outposts will doubtlessly have been bearing children for scores of years, but given the limited room on spacecraft, the human population at the end of the third millennium will still be tiny. Human technologies, such as nuclear powered chemical conversion plants, will surely be of significant importance to the planet's environment. But people's presence itself will still wield an almost insignificant direct influence upon the Martian global ecology when the terraforming project is completed.

Remember, in what I saw, the home planet is doomed. Hopefully, support from the home planet will persist to the completion of the terraforming program. But it is not likely to last very long after that point. Not if we judge either by the prophecy given me, or by reasonable projection of the rate of current Earth destruction. When Earth stops supplying Mars with technology, expertise, resources, and other support, any human Martian population will almost certainly revert to a status not unlike early man hundreds of thousands of years ago. For lack of bodies to maintain and repair them indefinitely, buildings and equipment already installed will simply rot away. It'll be the *Earth Abides* scenario played out for real, but on a different planet.

Gaia Abides, as it were.

Most likely it would take geologic time to put us back into the "driver's seat" on Mars, and, by then, maybe we will have evolved into a species more deserving of having survived planet Earth.

It borders on naivete to assume we will be persistent enough and lucky enough to place humans in a friendly, terraformed Martian environment. Had I not witnessed a Vision telling me that we need to attempt exactly that, I'd have rejected it out of hand myself. But I *did* see the Vision and my research since tells me it *is* possible, even if extraordinarily difficult. A success on the order of our being in any position to threaten another ecosystem, even one of our own, original construct, within a few thousand years, however, is simply not going to happen.

Despite the concerns of those most critical of the human history of misbehavior, it is appropriate to advocate going to Mars as an effort to save ourselves. Like every Lifeform, we have the instinctual urge to do just that.

But the Message of the Vision was that our greatest—our first—obligation is to assure that *some* form of life from Earth be preserved. This is the mantle we wear by virtue of our mastering technology: we are the only species even remotely capable of doing it. The part is smaller than the whole, and although we are only a very small part of the Gaian Lifeforce, our role is critical in its future. Our highest duty is to the whole.

What awaits us on planet Earth is not just an impending disaster for humans, threatening only our species, but a calamity for the biosphere beyond our most fearsome nightmares. The entire Lifeforce as we know it is under attack. That is *so* much greater than a threat to human survival. However, it is natural to expect humans to think of their own survival before anything else, and with that in mind, we must recognize that the time required to save humans from this impending disaster will be greater, by orders of magnitude, than that required to save *something*, so haste is imperative if we hope to save ourselves as well.

Aspects of the task of terraforming Mars may not be so daunting as the overall job itself, however. Simply transferring other Earth-based Lifeforms to Mars, such as the terraforganisms mentioned earlier, for example, is not nearly so difficult as transplanting humans will be. The aforementioned extremophiles are also obvious candidates for this purpose. Mars will have to undergo some extreme changes before even these Earth-based forms can survive, and accomplishing just that much will require a level of human support for space adventures both far greater and more directed toward development than is presently the case, but that task will clearly require much less alteration of the planet than would making it hospitable to humans.

Without some clear intent of preparing a way for humans, though, we ought not expect support for sending any such creatures to Mars. If we don't see a human benefit, we won't try at all. That's just the way we are.

But we don't need to worry about ruining Mars. The thought that that is even a possibility is just an alternate version of our universal tendency to see ourselves as the center of all things, unbounded and invincible. *Listen to me! We are going to be lucky if we get out of this alive.*

The Sinking Ship

The Earth has sometimes been likened to a sinking ship, as I did myself, earlier. It is an excellent simile. If this ship be made of wood, it has a severe infestation of termites–we humans. Currently, the only goal of the world's economic community is to accelerate the growth of the infestation. There is no land in sight and we have no lifeboat. There are no sister ships onto which we can scramble when ours goes down. Our environmental protection "pest control sprays" are all impotent, and there is presently no rescue equipment at all. We've no reason to think that any alien knows or cares that our ship is here. We can see the water level rising. No help is on the way. Our only chance is to build a lifeboat from the materials available to us.

The ultimate crisis in nautical tragedies is reached when the water rises to the point that it floods the engine, for without power the ship flounders helplessly. For us, that time will be when a lack of resources begins to stall the economic engine of capitalism. Fighting over remaining resources will doom any efforts to protect the Lifeforce itself. We humans will be worried only about our individual or, at best, our societal survival, as we already seem to be–as we have always seemed only to be.

I laud those who, thinking we can still save planet Earth, have long been committed to bailing water out of the bilge. This is the current status of the environmental community. I thank them. I support them both personally and monetarily. But they are fooling themselves if they think, as so many seem to, that they are holding their own. Our engine will soon be flooding. The crisis is close upon us.

Recognizing the validity of this analogy will, however, soon be irrelevant. If we wait until vital supplies are obviously running out–i.e., until the shortages are so evident that no one in power can deny it, or genocidal wars are routinely being waged between first world nations–it will be too late. Not only will there be even less public support than today for building an alternative living space millions of miles away, but we will have already lost the ability to do the job by virtue of no longer *having* the resources. The demands of resource competition will deprive us of *the* most crucial resource needed for accomplishing that goal: worldwide cooperation. In so doing it will also drive us to the Earth enshrouding war of which I spoke earlier.

We can no longer tolerate those who calmly talk about "scientific ambiguities" surrounding global warming, or appeal to economics and how industry needs time to accommodate the demands for cleaner air. Some doubters may, indeed, be qualified experts in their fields and sincere. But most are lying either to both themselves and us, or just to us. We must see through those liars and rely on the vast majority of scientists who are sounding the alarm.

We can see for ourselves. No "Vision" is required. Only our attention is necessary. *We have to stop ignoring these problems!*

As we speak, water rises toward the engine. Very soon it will be flooded. There will be no saving us. No building the lifeboat. Nothing but floundering. There will be no saving of *any*thing, let alone "the planet." Don't buy the bullshit. Bail!

Denial is natural, but we can no longer afford it. Our resources are quickly evaporating. Our opportunity to exit is shutting down. The task is much larger than we anticipate. Gaia is dying. We humans are killing Her. *We've got to get off!*

Absurd as it may have at first sounded, building the lifeboat is our *only* option. We *must* build a new planet. And we must start now–*right now*!

Easter Island, Easter Earth
As the Earth's population comes under more and more stress, dissension will grow and turn more violent, dwarfing our present concepts of genocide and civil war.

Governments will be totally absorbed in suppression of revolt and/or supplying/defending necessities, and the opportunity to develop a lifeboat will have been missed.

As mentioned earlier, Diamond's discussions in *Collapse* point to exactly this end. His treatment of the Easter Islanders, though, is particularly apropos. That society collapsed under numerous pressures, the largest of which were almost certainly a combination of deforestation, with its associated environmental impacts, and isolation, as Easter Island was completely cut off from other societies. As Diamond comments, "[Their] isolation probably also explains why I have found that their collapse, more than the collapse of any other pre-industrial society, haunts my readers and students. The parallels between Easter Island and the whole modern world are chillingly obvious."[38]

The parallels most apparent to me are religious and social beliefs that don't square with the realities of the environment, and blindness to the implications of unsustainable consumption of vital resources.

The Easter Islander's religion and social practices drove them to eradicate their forests: The large trees that once flourished there were harvested to move religious icons (the statues) from the quarry to sites scattered all around the island's coast, and the status of competing clans was associated with the number and ostentatiousness of these totems. Similarly, our unsustainable consumption of vital resources is driven chiefly by two factors: the societal dominance of capitalism, in which status is bestowed directly in proportion to how much one consumes, and the

---

[38]Diamond, *Collapse* pg. 119.

anachronistic practices of many religions and cultures in promoting population growth.

The blindness comparison may, at first blush, appear simpler than I mean it to be. The islanders apparently realized too late that the trees were vital resources whose loss would have devastating environmental impacts. The comparison with how cavalier so many analysts are today is obvious. Even the comparison of the role of the islanders' religion and our own beliefs as driving forces in our respective societies' obstinate adherence to untenable courses is apparent.

What is more subtle, however, and central to my theme, is occluded by our own difficulties in analyzing our present situation. Until after the fact, Easter Islanders probably never imagined the horrible implications the consumption of their forests would have for their population. When Europeans first encountered them, their numbers had declined massively from the days when they were raising statues and felling trees. Famine had obviously taken its toll in the meantime.

Yet some survived. No solace to those who didn't, of course, and the decline was such that even the survival of those that eventually did persist was not guaranteed.[39] At some point, the remaining people on that island wished fervently that there were enough large trees left to try to reach some other island. Early in the destruction of their forests, they lost the ability to build seaworthy vessels. When the remaining trees were so

---

[39]In 1872, after the additional devastation of disease and exploitation that came with contact with Europeans, there were only 111 native Easter Islanders still living. Diamond, *Collapse*, pg 112.

small that the islanders were stitching them together to build boats, the lack of sealing materials and/or expertise on the island resulted in vessels better described as colanders. They *couldn't* get off.

Not seeing any alternative to "saving the planet," most of us tend to think of their situation as being identical to ours. That's not true, however. They had numerous reasons to believe there were better places to go. They knew from oral tradition that they had come to the island from afar. They may even have retained the knowledge to survive for long periods on the high sea.

They were stuck, for sure, and so are we.

They were stuck, however, for very different reasons than are we. What they lacked was the *means* of getting off. If they had retained the ability to build boats, then the biggest problems would have been navigation and survival on the seas, both skills for which Polynesians were famous.

What we lack is *somewhere to go*. Certainly, there are plenty of landfalls within our reach–terrestrial bodies in outer space–but, unlike islands in the pacific ocean, none are habitable. We need to turn these rocks into gardens. At least one of the rocks.

And here is where the real decision of the third millennium comes; In Diamond's words, "Our situation today differs in important respects from that of Easter Islanders in the 17th century. Some of those differences increase the danger for us: if mere thousands of Easter Islanders with just stone tools and their own muscle power sufficed to destroy their environment, . . . how can billions of people with metal tools and machine power now fail to do worse? But there are also differences in our favor, differences to which we shall return in the last chapter of this book."[40]

Of course, in the last chapter of his book, Diamond lays out all the "there's still time" arguments he has in common with all of the other environmentalists to whom no one is listening.

Unfortunately, I have no such last chapter, for the Vision–and my observations of the reality of our present course–say there is *not* time left. It's too late. ***"We're not going to make it."***

Yet, Diamond is right in pointing out there are differences in our favor. He's even right in his list and what we can do to make the most of it (see his final chapter). The other hopeful environmentalists are also full of important suggestions for prolonging this planet's health. Suggestions we all need to begin heeding. But when I look for differences between the Easter Islanders and ourselves that work in our favor, the most hopeful I see is the fact that we are no longer in the stone age. While the Easter Islanders had lost the means of getting off, we're just beginning to develop the means of providing somewhere to go. The challenge, as I see it–the hope, actually–is to have the foresight and intelligence to prepare a place for which we can sail.

But the decision for you, dear reader, is clear: Either listen to Diamond et al, or listen to me. Then start *doing* something, either for his/their cause, or for mine. And start doing it *earnestly*.

All the standard environmental authors and I share this much: if people continue on the present course, we are doomed.

---

[40]Diamond, *Collapse* pg. 119.

Where I differ is in my understanding of the "we" who are doomed. I've seen a "we" so large that I can't morally defend risking "us" (big sense) on the slim chance that people are going to change their ways in time.

If you join with the environmentalists who still have hope for Earth, it helps my cause too, for it certainly buys time for Gaia, so God Bless you. But if you join neither of us, and continue on just as before, then God Damns us all![41]

Noah! Why Not Noah??

The Lifeforce itself is in danger here. This entire planet is going belly up. Gaia Herself is dying. No survivors of any kind, no plants, no animals–no amoeba, even. No worms at the bottom of the non-existent seas. I think I know why I, and so many others who've yet to come forward, have had this Vision. As crazy as it sounds, God, whatever that means, is trying to alert us so we, Gaia's only possible rescuers, will build a lifeboat. An Ark, if you will. My personal expectation is that humans will not be on board, that we do not have enough time. But that doesn't give us any excuse not to rise to our calling. It would be great if some of us (humans) get off–absolutely the most wonderful thing in the world. But it matters not at all. We *must* respond.

---

[41]Just an expression. Not meant to indicate I actually think that I understand the concept of "God," think He/She/It pays us any attention, or actively influences our planet in any way. But it's a useful expression to summarize the situation, nonetheless.

We must respond because we are the only creatures that can. We *must* try.

When Moses set out across the desert, his Mission was to lead the Israelites to a new "Promised Land." That is not at all our situation. For one thing, no real estate agent in the world could convince even the most gullible potential buyer that Mars was so much as a pleasant place for a second home, let alone a "Promised Land." Mars will be no picnic for those creatures that make it there. It'll be cold, dry, and dusty. Not at all the same thing as a Promised Land.

But, if we're waxing Biblical again, *this* planet, Earth, was our Promised Land, even our Garden of Eden. And we've trashed it. Ironically, we did so by disobeying the first commandment the Bible records: we partook fully of the "fruit of knowledge."[42] It is, after all, partaking of the fruit of knowledge whenever you use intelligence to gain a competitive edge–like being able to stay warm by building a fire; keeping the vegetables just for yourself by saving up the seeds and then putting up a fence around your garden; powering your numerous tools by damming rivers and building power plants; etc., etc. Perhaps appropriately, then, more like Adam and Eve than Moses and his meandering band, we are now condemned to lose the best thing we ever could have had. *If* we survive at all.

---

[42]The King James version always adds "of good and evil," but I've never seen it that way. I figure some clever cleric from antiquity added that phrase because it made more sense as an evil to him than "fruit of knowledge" alone. Not so to me.

Despite its emotional appeal, however, this imagery is all basically wrong. I may have seen the future in a Vision–and that certainly smacks of religion–but this is not about man's relationship with God. It's not about mysticism, and I am no Messiah. It's about physics and depletion of resources and the delicate balance of the Earth's ecosystem. It's about natural consequences, not divine intervention. But most of all, *it's not about humans.* Humans may be the species that have destroyed Earth's future, and they are certainly the only species with a chance of getting us–any of us–to a survivable alternative, but it is not, and never was *about* humans. It's about *Life*: the life of Gaia.

We humans *have* to get over ourselves. I'm talking about the death of the *planet.* Incomprehensible death. Incomprehensible.

It's Not about Giving Up

The Vision showed what will become of this planet. My assumption is that the continued abuse of the biosphere that humans are incapable of stopping will play a major role in Earth's demise. Whatever the cause, however, the Message was plain and stark: *"**We are not going to make it. We've got to get off!**"* That is not at all the same as "Let's set up deck chairs, strike up the band, and wait for the waves to take us home." In fact, were it not for this being a common reaction, I wouldn't speak to it at all, it seems so far off base. I am *not* calling on anyone to give up on this planet.

I am also not predicting the end of the Earth in our lifetimes, although I can't guarantee that, since the Vision contained no time line. But what would have been the point of sending the Message at all if there weren't enough time for a response? (Obviously a

"Gödel barrier" question–but one which I must, if I am to have hope, answer nonetheless. So I'm assuming we have some time left.)

Using the metaphor of the sinking ship, we have to keep it afloat long enough to build the lifeboat if we are to have any hope of abandoning ship. Materials are available, but time is critical. Even if we have as many as 900 years, it will be a close race. That's because even before we can expect to start the clock we must first build public support for terraforming Mars. That will mean years, probably decades, of preliminary work convincing the world that an alternative planet is our best bet. If we don't start exercising some real stewardship for this planet, there will simply not *be* enough time. Bailing to stave off the rising water in the bilge is a *very* crucial activity. My experience–the Vision–emphatically indicates bailing is only a stopgap measure for helping mother ship Earth, but we are talking about 300 to 900 years before the lifeboat can possibly be ready for us. So someone had sure as hell better be attempting to patch the thousands of leaks or we are doomed, indeed. Stewardship may be too late to *save* the ship, but it's absolutely necessary if we hope to save *ourselves*.

Each of us can only do our part, however. Most of us are totally incapable of making the dream of a lifeboat possible. All we can do is reuse, recycle, reduce our consumption of resources, oppose the environmental destruction lobby (EDL), and make sacrifices in whatever other ways may become apparent in promoting both the development of Mars *and* the preservation of Earth. In addition we can apply constant pressure on our peers, business contacts, and politicians to do the same. But someone else has to get going on the project of actually building the lifeboat. All most of us can contribute to that highly specialized task is our consistent agitation–and our total commitment to preserving Earth as long as possible. Environmentalism must be our banner. It's not some fad or a recreational activity. It's part of our "job description."

There is a small set of environmentalists who already take environmentalism this seriously, although most of them don't have any patience for talk of "abandon ship" at all. Earth First! and the Earth Liberation Front (ELF) have made headlines in recent years by their willingness to take violent action against the EDL. I'll speak to violence and why it is so extremely counterproductive later, but suffice it to say here that *all* environmentalists need to take their environmentalism as much to heart as do these few dedicated, if misguided, activists.

Whether you believe in the Vision I saw or not, if you claim to be a true environmentalist, please recognize the extreme danger we are in. I join you all in saying, "God forbid that those trying to save the Earth should fail." What if they do fail, though, and what if the consequences of failure *are* total destruction of the ecosystem itself, as the Vision foretold? Then, without another world for Earthlings to inhabit, *all* is lost. I believe in the truth of what I was shown, but even for the nonbeliever, the risk is simply too great to ignore.

One need not agree with my sense of inevitability to recognize the consequences of failure and, therefore, to share my sense of urgency. Nor does one need share my conviction that we must abandon ship to recognize that it is sinking and how quickly. At present, the EDL controls government, industry, religion, and the media. Therefore, the consumption of Earth's resources continues to be encouraged by every major institution of our culture.

To change that, the option of having the lifeboat to fall back on must be recognized, accepted, and encouraged. Until environmentalists take their own claims seriously enough to endorse a real plan B, no one else will take their concerns very seriously either, and the Julian Simonses[43] of the world will continue to feed the EDL fallacious counter arguments, helping them to rationalize staying on the course to disaster.

There is much we humans can do to postpone the inevitable, however. Virtually everything which is currently thought of as "saving the planet" or "green" is in this category. It will *not* save the Earth, but it will, hopefully, *preserve* it long enough to save Gaia. Our only option is to get off this planet and our only hope is to keep it alive long enough to do that.

If we are to succeed in getting off, we will need every moment of whatever breathing room environmentalists can get us. However, if we continue in our denial of the true danger that humans represent, not only to ourselves but to Gaia Herself, then our chance of succeeding is nil. The window of opportunity for that realization is small.

Environmentalists need to support terraforming Mars. Until they do, they are only making that first, impotent, "won't you please help me" call. We must all listen to how we sound now as we plead Gaia's case. It's time to realize our need to show convincing alarm. *Nobody* is listening! There's *absolutely* no panic in our voices. What if they don't *believe* us???

---

[43]See footnote 37, page 3-108

Beyond War

One positive that can, and *must,* come from the Vision, then, is a much more invigorated environmental movement. There are also some benefits of trying seriously to "get off" which may not have been central, previously, to the environmental movement, but which should have been. The foremost of these is the necessity of world peace, as pointed out in the discussion of space junk above. The bad news, of course, is that, to succeed in getting us off the planet, we've simply *got* to end war–something mankind has attempted innumerable times, never with a hint of success.

The good news is that one of the major contributing factors to the continued practice of war, namely the war economy, may be defused. Terraforming Mars could become an enlightened substitute for war. We may be able to alter the role war has played in the world's economy. The great depression of 1929 ended only when World War II began a decade later. That was not an accident.

After the stock market crash of 1929, business ground to a halt and no one had money to buy anything. Capitalist societies are built upon consumption and growth. As long as there is a market for the stuff you're making, there's a job to be had and money to spend, assuring a market. What made the depression so tenacious was the lack of people with enough money to get the market started again.

War is the greatest of all (traditional) consumers. Build things merely for the purpose of destroying the things your opponents have built with the exact mirror purpose. Manufacturing, essentially, with the sole intent of tearing the products up. From the industrialist's point of view, that's the whole advantage of going to war. War is absolutely *great* for business. No wonder the wealthy often seem enthused when their nations get into shooting matches. That and the fact that their own kids rarely have to risk their lives. Add to this the fact that governments will literally print the money necessary to pay for it, and war is the obvious solution to a serious depression.

The potential downside of war, from the economist's viewpoint, is its zero sum nature: the victor walks away with the prize, be it territory, resources, or dominion, while losers are killed, impoverished, enslaved, or otherwise used or abused by the victors. There's nothing "win-win" about it.

Why the military-industrial complex has not recognized the potential of space exploration as a substitute for war and done something to exploit it is baffling to me. Space exploration is the only other modern market in which hugely expensive toys are constructed for the sole purpose of being destroyed or discarded. And, unlike war, no one has to be attacked, no one slaughtered, no piece of the Earth rendered uninhabitable and, perhaps best of all, one doesn't have to worry about the nasty possibility that "*They*" might win.

Neither is it as if space exploration were in competition with the war industry. The beneficiaries of space exploration are, and will always remain, the same entities that benefit most from military spending. The rockets that carry warheads are ideal for carrying landing modules. The makers of unmanned drones are naturals to do Mars rovers. Men and women whose experience is rooted in the adversity and discipline of warfare are the people best qualified to deal with the dangers of outer space.

Nor is it that there are no natural resources in the larger universe to be harvested. There's reason to believe, or so I've read in what appear to be authoritative places, that it rains diamonds on Saturn. (Just don't quote me on that specific, please, as it decidedly smacks of wishful thinking.) But even moon rocks would draw a fortune if the government would just put them up for sale. True, the cost of retrieval from space may currently be immense, but that should come down with technological advances.

Perhaps industrialists' preference for war over space is really driven by a common misperception of the relative size of the potential markets. As currently practiced, space may seem like a rather limited source of income to those whose bread and butter is weapons systems. And rightfully so, for the current space program *is* tiny in comparison to the military. But, if taken seriously, terraforming Mars would dwarf warfare as we know it. Here lies an arena of even greater potential consumption than war can ever be, for the boundaries of space are literally infinite and the cost is not counted in millions of souls destroyed. You'd think industrialists of every sort would enthusiastically get behind the manned space program.

Probably what scares them off is the lack of *public* commitment to the project, for without it, there's no engine to keep the wheels turning.

That leads us to the only place where war trumps space exploration: in motivating the public. The advantage for militarism is especially pronounced when the focus of space exploration is merely investigating the unknown. Wonder is not nearly so rousing as fear. And fear is never stronger than when it takes the form preferred by war mongers throughout history: hate. Hatred is a classic example of an autocatalytic phenomenon, for it regenerates itself, magnified, in the hearts of its victims, who invariably retaliate in like kind. Curiosity, on the other hand, bores the witness and can even try the patience of practitioners.

In most people's minds, the most compelling objection to the manned space program seems to be the claim there is no valid rationale for using humans at all. Robots can perform scientific exploration, the opponents quite correctly say, more easily and cost-effectively than humans. If we only want information, there is no need for us to go into space at all.

Space advocates cannot appeal only to wonder at the infinite mystery of space and expect to flourish; that's simply not a good enough reason.

But that's *not* the reason we should be looking at outer space. Not at all.

Until Earthlings of some sort go there, in the sense of "emigrate," Life in this portion of the universe is not secure. We'll also need robots, of course, but the real burden of "going there" must be borne by humans. Only by sending humans to Mars permanently, or by trying to, can we focus our efforts on survival. That is the real reason for a manned space program. We must begin to move from simple exploration to the next level, development, with all haste. Only people can do that.

Look around you. We are killing the Earth. We *are*. And we *will not* stop. We cannot control the one thing that is causing it: our population. The human species will never voluntarily reduce itself back to the size it was, say, before the industrial revolution. The reason? We can't. We can't because our cultural traditions, laws, morals, and habits all developed over eons in an environment in which the well-being of Homo sapiens was best served through growth. Just the opposite is true today, but we're stuck with the culture that we've got. Ironically, it is the inertia of our own glorious success which propels us toward tragic, colossal failure.

We have been blinded by a religious/cultural history of looking at our species' bloom as being "the ascent of man," It's past time to truly ascend–to recognize our part in this wonderful whole as no more than exactly that: a part.

We are not merely going to ruin it for us but for *all* Gaians. That is a motivational force as great as any. It is the motivation of love. Love for the Lifeforce as we know it. Love for Gaia.

Is This A Self-fulfilling Prophecy?

One of the legitimate objections that comes up when people first encounter my Message is, "If you aren't giving up, then at least you are certainly in danger of hastening the decline." The reasoning seems to be that by offering no long-term hope of saving the planet itself, I am encouraging a "what the Hell, I might as well trash it now" attitude.

I don't see it that way. First, that seems to be the attitude of the vast majority of people anyway, so I don't see how my pointing out the course on which we are clearly already bound will do much harm. Secondly, as I've already indicated, it's neither my intent that people stop working to save the planet, nor my expectation that realizing the likelihood of losing that fight will lead people to stop "bailing and patching." Not if they recognize the possibility of building the lifeboat. Before the essential rationing that may buy us the time to build the escape option can start, however, people have to believe in the likelihood of complete destruction of the supply. I'm just the one who's raising the alarm.

The concept of rationing ourselves may seem to run directly against the current economic standard, capitalism. The conflict is real and must be acknowledged, for the general population certainly cannot continue unbridled on its current path if there is to continue to be a path at all. That won't destroy the economy. On the contrary, it will merely redirect and intensify our economic activity.

Terraforming Mars will consume vast resources, just as Pann used up a great deal of body hydration walking out of danger behind my house.[44] There must be no rationing when it comes to the project of "getting off;" no reasonable expense should be spared. Those resources, though, must be invested in solving the problem, not wasted. Sitting here eating up Earth's remaining resources is very much like sleeping in would have been for Pann and I: it will kill us if we don't realize what we're doing and stop it. Consumption just for its own sake, which is apparently the current goal of the capitalist world, must, however, be eliminated altogether. Pann got all the water he indicated he wanted that day, but I stepped on every urge to think or speak of the thirst that roiled under my surface. Pann's mobility was the issue, not mine. Keeping Earth alive as long as possible, and preparing an escape route are the issues today, not having a "cool" car, or a cool office in a hot city, or any of the other luxuries we, individually, love.

Unlike with Pann and I, though, the resources used in going to Mars will be an asset in our rescue: it will drive a strong economy. Despite the fact the average person will be forced to conserve, the terraforming project will bring a huge economic boom.

---

[44]See the section On How Rationing Works.

Rationing was part and parcel of America's experience in the Second World War, after all, and that didn't kill the national prosperity that went with it. That we need the everyday citizen to be rationing resources is not at all contradictory to the claim that the economy will go into overdrive. The Mars development project will be the engine propelling a world-wide commercial expansion perhaps greater than any seen before. We need to regard this exactly like a war effort! If we don't recognize the impending threat of this planet truly dying, we'll never move to the point of rationing in time.

Finally, one last thought: what I'm telling you is that the end of the planet is *happening*. It is happening **now**. Continuing to ignore that fact accelerates the process. Our only chance of surviving is to *stop* ignoring both the fact and the ultimate consequence. Pann and I didn't ration the water until we saw the need. Humans will not ration our resources until we see the need.

So long as we harbor the fantasy that the universe is *about* human beings, we will be unable to recognize our true circumstance. The first step toward Mars, then, is to give that idea up. No, even before that, we must learn to recognize it every time it slips out, as it does so frequently that you'll be flabbergasted once you start watching for it.

A powerful way of debunking our human-centric view of the universe is to go outside on a dark night, preferably far from city lights, and look up at the stars. We now know what they are, how far away they are, how they move and what causes them to burn. In particular, we know they do not revolve around us. The ancients, who wrote *all* of the religious texts we still regard as divine, did not know any of that.

Their words often still hold great relevance for how to treat one another, for they understood people as well as we do today. But can you support the most basic assumption of most of those old religions about what our place is in the universe–that we are the reason it was created? Can you support that position knowing it is precisely the attitude which is leading us to destroy the planet on which we live?

I certainly cannot. I will no longer use the belief that the universe was created *for* humans as a justification for the destruction of the rest of the only Lifeforce we know.

Chapter 4
Into The Wilderness

Everything I Ever Needed To Know,
I Learned At The Shore
Terri, my second wife, died of cancer in 1988.
She was only forty-three. We were divorced by then,
and both had other relationships, but her death bore an
unwelcome finality that, combined with the Vision,
contributed to a profound and prolonged depression. I
spent considerable time at isolated beaches that year
grieving both losses. One day a family came down to
play nearby, and three or four children began delightedly
playing tag with the surf. Instead of my usual pleasure
at watching happy children, it struck me how innocent
they were of the powers beyond our control. Playing tag
with the ocean, as if it couldn't swat you dead on a
whim. The slightest variation of wave activity could
easily have snatched those children away.

The ocean, vast beyond the ability of the human
mind to conceive, is to our largest cities as a skyscraper
is to a gnat. When we play with it, we count upon its
indifference. We trust that it is not about to notice
us–that it is completely oblivious to our existence. If
there were *any* likelihood that it would notice us there
upon its shore enjoying its presence in our own ways, we
would not tease it by playing tag, or any other game. We
would hide.

Yet we seem oblivious to the apparent fact that
the Earth, in its entirety, is beginning to notice our
existence. After all, that's what it amounts to when our
activities begin to register on a worldwide scale.

The tsunami of December 2004 only hints at the
kind of power we are dealing with when discussing such
topics as global warming or depletion of the ozone layer.

The energies of nature are incomprehensibly immense. Because we've met and "mastered" most of her daily manifestations, however, and have always swum in her waters, we are now almost entirely oblivious to her. Only when she occasionally unleashes her destructive side, as in that catastrophic wave–or a hurricane, flood, earthquake, or tornado–do we pay her any mind whatever. What may not be obvious, unless you look closely, is that the horrific tragedy of that tsunami was tiny compared to the utter devastation of the Vision. The worst tsunami can only be a very slight intimation. No event known to man, in fact, compares.

The tsunami was triggered by a 9.0 suboceanic earthquake. That's large for an earthquake, but, on the global scale, earthquakes are only local phenomena. This one was barely felt outside the nearest landmasses, Sumatra and Thailand. Even the impact of the tsunami it created was merely regional. Since only low-lying land was affected, it's safe to say that the portion of the Earth's surface which was significantly impacted was far less than a thousandth of the total.

Yet it was the largest disaster to strike the Earth in several lifetimes. The largest that has already run its full course, at least. What we don't know is whether the events set in motion via the huge success of the human species, events such as the gradual CO_2 loading of the atmosphere, constitute a disaster on a global scale still in the making–yet at sea, so to speak.

The tidal wave of 2004 also illustrates quite vividly the ways in which a series of relatively small interconnected events can multiply their effects to produce a major catastrophe far beyond any one of them: a boulder somewhere in the rift between two tectonic plates is crushed by the building pressure of continental drift, starting a chain of other crushed boulders. The fault gives way; suboceanic soil slides; water rushes from one space to another at great depth. The surface roils and the disturbance spreads, becoming an expanding circular hump on the surface of a relatively calm sea. Crossing hundreds of miles of open ocean without a visible sign until, on shores most suited to accentuate a wave from just that direction, the sea suddenly pulls back far from the land and at last, the swell shows itself, rushing back toward the land and cresting as people who were innocently going about their business or pleasure in idyllic little coastal villages all around the basin look up in surprise and horror. Finally, the wave strikes with a fury unparalleled in human experience.

How dare we ignore the early warning signs of global impacts of human activity! We have pricked the giant with our incessant growth, and climate change and ozone depletion and dead spots in the oceans are its first twitches as it begins to stir—water shifting from one space to another, as it were. Our governments, obsessed with money and human-centered power, count their little collection of shells while the tide begins to draw back, exposing the sea floor as the ocean rises behind it. Human-centered "power," indeed—just wait until crops no longer grow, or *all* the fresh water disappears—and not just in some isolated places. Therein lies "power." Our governments are infantile, like babies at the shore. And none is more puerile than my own, the U.S.A., which has the body and the strength of a young adult, but the mind of a two-year-old.

Some things are obvious. One did not have to read a headline to see the tsunami crest as it rushed to shore at Phuket. No one who saw the oncoming water would have waited for a government-approved siren, had there been one in place to sound a warning. No one seeing it would have heeded a politician's denial even if the governments of the Indian Ocean's perimeter had noticed the earthquake and still disputed the facts, like too many of America's "leaders" are today denying the reality of global warming. But just as surely as people would not have paid any attention to official attempts to veil the reality of the tsunami once they could see it cresting for themselves, so, too, will waiting until we all see the impact of global warming–or whatever it is that eventually does us in–be too late.

Climate change and ozone depletion and dead regions in the seas and who knows what else are, admittedly, not as obvious as a cresting wave. Not yet. These are the first signs of the building stress load. The real disaster is far more likely to manifest itself when some small "boulder" in the system is crushed. Something like a drought sending a fragile regional tropical forest to its grave, or an undersea volcano venting naturally occurring green house gases into the atmosphere, suddenly tipping the already borderline balance of chemicals past a critical point, triggering unforseen consequences on an unprecedentedly devastating scale.

We do have a system for monitoring Earth-wide variations, however: the scientific community. It is rather long-range, though whether or not it is adequately long-range is doubtful (the Vision and the current political climate say it is not). To that community, it is obvious that there are real, *human-caused*, changes occurring on this planet–changes of a global scope and having the potential of incomprehensible impacts.[45]

---

[45] See, for example, the editorial by
Naomi Oreskes, *The Scientific Consensus on*

The army of agents of the corporate world confuses the issue with its cadence of denial and obfuscation. There is little profit motive for recognizing an impending world-wide disaster. Tranquility is better for business: doing nothing, on the short term, costs nothing, and who knows about the future? Especially a future as remote as 300+ years. Even businesses don't plan that far in advance. Worrying about it can only interfere with today's profits. Hence the EDL's[46] persistent efforts to assuage our concerns. That their motives are self-serving and their goal abstruseness *is* obvious, and it is *imperative* that we convince the greater community to ignore them and to pay attention to the vast majority of scientists instead. That some of the corporate-industrial-government's cadre masquerade as legitimate scientists is as irrelevant as it is disappointing.

It's time we look up from our mundane activities, see the tell-tale signs of a receded sea, and yell, "Run! Run for your lives!"

A Reality Check (2):
On the Natural Collapse of Humanity
The Vision predicted that the planet Earth is doomed.

Logic, and the data, have long argued a case for the eventual collapse of the *human* population. The explosive growth of Homo sapiens is an undeniable fact. Everything in our history, science, and character, suggests that we will not, and cannot, do anything to

---

Climate Change, Science, Vol. 306, December 3, 2004, pg 1686.

[46]The "Earth Destruction Lobby."

reverse, or even stop, our growth. It's worth mentioning that most human institutions attain much of their power by encouraging a large growth rate amongst their devotees. Perhaps the most glaring and aggressive example is the Catholic Church, but almost all religions, most countries and even families also adopt the tactic. In the "survival of the fittest" competition that rules ideologies as surely as it dominates evolution, this strategy has powerful appeal. It is precisely these institutional pressures for growth that make population impossible to control in a modern, urban society.

The resources on planet Earth are finite, however. One can bicker about how long we can make them last, but arguing for "forever" is ludicrous. Extraterrestrial resources will not be available for use on this planet in the foreseeable future. And, as I've already shown, the window for tapping into them at all may be severely limited. Humans are in for a major set back. That much seems certain.

Because of the global impact of human activity, and the evidence from Mars, my scenario–that view revealed to me in a Vision–that the Earth itself will cease to harbor life of any kind, is *not* unreasonable.

But no one looks at the now well established fact that Mars lost water, temperature, and atmosphere and asks "Hmmmm, I wonder if *Earth's* water, temperature, and atmosphere are secure?" Why don't they? Because those things just *have* to be okay. If they're not, then it's "Rapture time." Hallelujah.

Besides, it's much more entertaining to wonder if life might have existed or, better yet, might still exist on Mars. And, hey, if *"it's"* not about entertaining and informing *us*, then what could it be about? The ultimate Gödel barrier question–again.

We can no longer embrace philosophies and strategies whose ultimate outcomes are not success, but complete and utter failure, no matter how entrenched in our culture they may be.

In a purely human-centric view, the specter of global changes threatening human extinction is apparent. Yet virtually no serious advocate of space exploration mentions the possibility that our very survival might be the primary reason for going to other worlds. No one is talking about terraforming Mars with the urgency implied in the term "lifeboat."[47]

We are trying merely to find out the secrets of the universe, or else just moving relentlessly forward toward our next manifest destiny. We've all the time in the world. Why? Because if we were to perish, well, that's the end of the story. Who cares whether Life itself goes on without us?

We have little interest, it seems, in assessing whether we might be endangering something even more important than ourselves: Gaia. We humans are simply too invested in the idea that the entire universe is all about us, and therefore nothing will happen to it which is not all about our God doing His/Her/Its thing for, or to, us. We believe that there *is* nothing more important

---

[47]Obviously, some advocates for terraforming Mars cite the added security that dual planet status gives as one of their rationales. But, until Stephen Hawking came public on this issue in June of 2006, (see footnote 26 page 3-88) none that I knew of advocated terraforming on the basis of a need to prepare a means, essentially, of abandoning Earth.

than us. Like cancer cells, most of us, buried so deeply in the interior, cannot see beyond the tumor.

It ought to mortify us. Such selfishness shames our species beyond description. Are we *completely* amoral?

Stemming The Tide

All the efforts that are currently directed at the problems of a deteriorating ecosystem deal, at most, with mitigation of the effects of the human infestation from which this planet suffers. No effort, except the ill-fated Zero Population Growth movement[48], has been aimed at stemming the infestation . Even ZPG failed to advocate *reduced* population, which is our real need.

Here's a few of the things that have been tried, and how they fail:

* Stop the increase in CO_2 and CFC releases in the atmosphere. Find substitutes even, but never lower the demand for either. Just meet that demand in some other, hopefully, more innocuous way.

* Reintroduce endangered species into habitats which, under the continued stress of relentless expansion of human habitats, are themselves inevitably destined for eradication.

* Set aside small ecological preserves amidst the increasingly vast ruins of resource

---

[48]I realize that ZPG still exists as an organization and probably still hopes to see its goals attained. But then, technically, at this writing, so does the original Common Sense.

extraction, but never stem the need for more extraction.

* Ban DDT (in *most* locales and for *most* purposes) but never reduce the need for increasingly higher crop yields.

* Promote buying "environmentally friendly" products, but never discourage the buying.

* Find alternatives to petroleum based fuel, but relentlessly increase energy consumption. (What *are* we going to do when our windmills proliferate to the point they affect the global circulation of the atmosphere??[49])

Fingers in dikes with no recognition of the dam's impending total failure. Symptoms, never the disease.

Even regarding the overwhelming success of humanity as an infestation is considered heretical. "Infestations" are understood to be by critters or microbes, not *us*. Seriously suggesting that our success is the "success" of a cancerous growth that will kill the total organism is simply not done in polite company.

---

[49]Ridiculous!?? What would Peter Stuyvesant, the early director of the Dutch colony on Manhattan Island, have thought had someone painted a picture of today's NYC and tried to tell him that was the future? We need to stop dismissing scenarios mostly because we don't want to confront their possibility. Unlimited population plus *any* kind of power generation equals *some* kind of disaster.

But I've never cared much for polite company, so let's go down that path a bit.

Cancer

To engage this image fully, let's start with the basics: cancer occurs when some particular cell in the body goes into an uncontrolled growth mode and co-opts the resources of the other cells in its vicinity, then of the whole body. If not treated in time, most cancers will kill the larger organism of which it is part. Many kinds of cells may turn malignant, but only two types of treatment, removal or destruction in place, seem to be effective. Arresting the growth is usually only a temporary measure. Many types of cancer can't be excised, especially after the disease has progressed sufficiently far. With such cases the attempts to kill the cancer usually involve systemic treatment which causes massive damage to the overall health of the individual.

The cell is to our body much as each of us is to the Earth–or, more accurately, to Gaia. This model, "Cell to human, human to Gaia" can very successfully be extended to a much higher level that speaks fairly well to some of what I've been trying to get at here:

A single cell is to the human being in which it lives as a human being is to Gaia;

and as Gaia is to the galaxy;
and as the galaxy is to the universe;
and,

perhaps,
as the universe is to God.

And through it all flows the Lifeforce.

Perhaps this is as close as we can ever come to understanding "God." Perhaps God *is* the Lifeforce. (Gödel just keeps popping up here, doesn't he?)

To elucidate: we know, or at least we think we know, that a liver cell, say, has no comprehension of what it means to be the person whose liver cell it is. By the same token, I think it absurd that humans don't recognize their own inability to comprehend what the planet is about. From the liver cell's point of view, the self-awareness of the whole person cannot, by the most generous stretch of the imagination, be recognized, let alone understood. When an enzyme is released into the world of the liver cell, the liver cell reacts, but it has no understanding of what brought the enzyme down on it, or how, or for what purpose. From the liver cell's perspective, it is an act of God. Or at the least, a tsunami triggered by a distant earthquake.

If humans are to be likened unto cells in Gaia's body, then we cells have gone into overtime growth mode, just like any of the cancers we all know and dread. Unless our population is somehow limited, our current path leads inevitably to our killing the larger whole, Gaia. (That is, perhaps, not obvious, but it *is* what the Vision implied.)

For years I anticipated self-excision via nuclear war or just the accumulation of our own waste and/or as the natural consequence of our consuming all available resources. I have imagined our growth being arrested by plague or pestilence, etc. Any review of futuristic fiction shows I'm far from alone in this regard.

If you look carefully, you'll notice that most environmentalists seem more concerned about preventing the various scenarios of self-excision than about assuring true sustenance for Gaia. They are reacting more to the danger we pose to ourselves than to any danger we pose to Gaia. I'm not saying that's not a legitimate concern, only that they're not at all the same thing, and that my concern differs from most currently being expressed.

Until I saw the Vision, I subscribed to that same, limited concern. But the Vision showed an entire planet that has already reached the terminal stage. In one sense, it was merely a diagnosis/prognosis. From that moment forward, my perspective has been very different.

In The Service of Gaia
In another sense, however, the Vision is not so much diagnosis, as a call to recognize and honor an even higher version of the Gaia Hypothesis than Lovelock and his successors have proposed: it is not just that the Earth Herself is alive, but that the Life She hosts is *itself* an entity. We are called upon to preserve this, the essence of Gaia, by getting Her off this planet. If we succeed we instill Her with a kind of immortality. If we don't, She dies.

This is the Gaia we are called upon to serve. The Gaia that is Life itself. I pass this call on to you with the only authority I have: the Vision.

My logical abilities are clearly no match for the questions these speculations raise. *No one's* are: that's the lesson of Gödel. Only the Vision seems to me to have any firmament upon which to stand. It was, after all, like a flush of enzyme flowing over my being. I don't know where it came from or why I encountered it, or even what it is, but its effect is obvious and overwhelming. Like the liver cell, I must respond.

The Mind of The Liver Cell
I'm endlessly amused by the reactions I get to the "liver cell" analogy–this comparing of a liver cell's view of its human to our view of God. They are often based

on yet another version of the "it's all about us" myth. "Liver cells don't think! They're not capable of rational behavior. They have no brain! What *are* you going on about??"

My response is simply, "Says who?"

Sure, the idea that a cell can understand the body is absurd. However, it is no more absurd than the idea that *we* understand God, or for that matter, that we understand the liver cell. How do we know any more about what a liver cell does or does not think than it is going to know about what we do or do not think? We have no idea—zip—nada—zilch—zero—what thinking is.

Oh, in humans, primates, and other macro species, we have traced a great many neural activities which we know occur simultaneously with the process and which we assume somehow embody it. We can identify parts of the brain that go into electrical activity when certain kinds of cognitive functions are being performed. We can do CAT scans and MRI's of the brain and spinal cord in an effort to pin down the physiological phenomena accompanying thought. We can stimulate various parts of the brain and record the subject's responses, often including forgotten memories. But none of these investigations—*none* of them—address, in the least way, what thinking *is*. We have no more of an understanding of thinking than we do of self-awareness, or Life itself.

The fact that we cannot identify activities in a cell which parallel those activities we associate with our own thinking is more an indication of the limits of our technology and—even more yet, of our imagination's inability to accept the possibility of a need for such investigations—than it is of any objective evidence of the absence of "thinking" on the part of the cell. Cells respond to enzymes and hormones, don't they? Who's to say they don't think on it first?

It's a *mystery*! Get used to it. Given the chain of parallelisms I've listed above with man buried deep at the start, what a laugher it is that we are incessantly trying to describe the mind of God. Ha, ha, ha! It may not relieve the depression into which this whole environmental topic sends thoughtful people every time it comes up, but it's a hell of a lot more honest to admit to our ignorance than what you're going to get from the priest, preacher, imam, or rabbi.

All questions like these seem firmly bound up in the "Gödel barrier."

As I mentioned earlier, mathematicians universally prefer a consistent system to a complete one. This seems like a clear place where we've assumed more knowledge than we can be assured is safe. When we pretend assumptions reflect facts, we invite contradictions throughout our belief system. Best to just let it go, I say.

If we are to establish a movement to last generations, we'll need a philosophical basis upon which to build that does not invite contradictions, and it's time to make a foundation of deeply driven piles, not crumbling bricks set in mud. Many questions in real life, if they are to be answered at all, seem obviously to require a complete system. I think almost any variation of "What's God like?" rises to this level. So, too, does the more facetious question of what the liver cell might, or might not, think. For people who prefer consistency, attempting to answer such questions is misguided. Better for them to proceed cautiously. The danger is that, in answering such questions, one probably is accepting as axiomatic beliefs which, if also ascribed to in other aspects of one's life, will lead to contradictory conclusions. How to determine which questions are beyond answering without introducing contradictions, however, is always problematic.

Gödel Revisited

In the Judaic-Christian-Muslim tradition, a common method of coping with excesses of axioms is to rank, usually subconsciously, the beliefs themselves. "Thou shalt keep the Sabbath day," lies lower on almost everyone's list than "thou shalt not kill." (It is, however, universally understood that to murder someone on the Sabbath is truly loathsome.)

Ranking, or tiering, is really not such a bad solution to the problem, but it needs to be acknowledged so that one is not constantly placed in the position of having to hedge one's axioms. An axiom is only truly an axiom if it is *always* regarded as being correct.

In my experience, most people simply select which of the competing beliefs is more acceptable–which *feels* more correct in the given situation–sort of an unconscious subscription to "situational ethics"–and never admit to a need to abandon *any* of their "deeply held" beliefs. Everyman just doesn't seem to rank consistency very highly.

We all choose our axioms based on our observations of the world. And people make their observations from vastly differing perspectives. Rationalists, like myself, have an entirely different way of observing than do mystics. The same can be said of people from very different cultures, or having different languages, for both influence greatly how one thinks. And, of course, as Cyndi Lauper sang, "money changes everything,"[50] so we ought not assume that rich and poor, even from the same cultures or religions, will have developed the same, or perhaps even a very similar, set of axioms.

Here mathematics can provide a valuable lesson. When mathematicians work with differing sets of axioms, as they frequently do, they construct different mathematical systems. There are, for example, three distinctly different geometries, Euclidean, Spherical, and Hyperbolic.

All three, on the scale of our everyday existence, coincide very nicely with our observed reality. This is possible because of the immensity of the scales required to actually observe differences. We think our world is Euclidean if we focus only on what we can see from the cabin of a cruise ship. If, however, we change our perspective by looking at Earth from outer space, we can see that we live on a surface which is not flat at all, but spherical. The Spherical Geometry is the best mathematical model to describe physical properties on the surface of the globe, but if we only explore a small portion of the sphere's surface, we lose almost nothing by assuming it is flat. Only when you begin to travel over large portions of the globe does using spherical geometry become important.

It may be that even the scale of the solar system is too small to adequately describe the larger universe. There the most accurate Geometry may well be the Hyperbolic. So far as our individual lives are concerned, though, all three systems are perfectly good descriptions of our everyday reality–so long as your daily reality

---

[50]Cyndi Lauper, *She's So Unusual* Portrait Records, CBS 1983.

doesn't involve trips to the other side of the globe, galaxy, or universe.

One system is not so much better than another as simply different. Euclidean Geometers tolerate the non-Euclidean Geometers and vice versa. To each his own. So, too, may differing sets of basic assumptions about the world lead to different conclusions about spiritual, existential, or philosophical reality without necessarily being discernibly better, one over the other, in describing the small portion of these constructs that are within the conceptual abilities of human beings.

Changing perspectives in the context of physics really amounts to breaking barriers of movement. Until humans sailed the open seas, there was no need to question Euclid's system. Our recent ventures into outer space now invite another review of the question. But in matters of philosophy, changing perspective is a more obscure concept than mere physical movement. If I were to venture *any* guess about what happens after death, it would be that (if we're aware of anything at all) it involves an extraordinary change in perspective.

From the perspective of this life, however, there are many possible explanations of what life is all about which simply cannot be decided. Our inability to perceive from those greater scales we hope to attain after death forces us into a position where there is simply no way to determine whether one set of axioms about God, or philosophy–or even morality–is more "true" than another. They are simply different. One religion's viewpoint is never *provably* better than another. They are just different attempts to describe reality.

When I speak of the "Gödel barrier," I'm referring to our inability to answer many of life's intriguing questions. Tolerance of systems which adopt differing axioms from our own, so long as they are tolerant of you, is the only rational way to proceed.

That is not to say that one cannot go ahead and make religious assumptions. It merely means that you should realize how very tenuous *any*one's beliefs are. Faith is very different from knowledge. Faith should always be held out as more hope than fact. We live our lives, always, on hope. We cannot help it, for it is the nature of our existence. But when we confuse faith with fact, we curse ourselves and others with contradictions and conflicts that, far too often, lead to tragedy.

First Principles

The mathematicians' model suggests that beginning with a small, unambiguous list of axioms and guarding against inconsistencies of every sort is the only hope for developing a solid belief system. Tiering may serve as a valuable compromise accommodating the desire to have guidance on a greater range of questions than strict adherence to consistency would allow.

If we use tiering, however, it seems obvious that the only way to avoid inconsistencies is to strictly limit the number of axioms in the highest tiers and to never reorder the priorities. I cannot imagine that, in a consistent system, tier one can have many more than two axioms. One assumption seems more crucial than any other: Life is a phenomenon so precious that it must be preserved. Not an individual's life, mind you. Not even human life or the life of any particular species. But the *phenomenon* of Life itself. Whatever it costs, Life, in this capital letter sense, must be preserved. That is my axiom number one, top tier.

Also, in any system I would support, admonition against greed would either be incorporated into the highest echelons or be an easy theorem to derive from them. Not greed in the monetary sense alone, but in the sense of wanting more of anything than you really need. More of Earth's natural resources, for example. And not just more than your "fair" share as a part of the human species: more than you *need*. Introducing axioms is a strong temptation, and we must learn to do so reluctantly, lest we accidentally introduce inconsistencies.

Most importantly, you should understand completely that this book and this new philosophy is not about people. Life is the phenomenon we honor, not Human life. Our Movement is about Life itself. About Gaia.

Why the "Einsteins" Don't Get This

I promised earlier to explain why it is that many "rocket scientists" don't seem to get this whole idea. I really can only speak to why western geniuses seem so dull-minded when it comes to the topic of the end of Life on Earth, but I think I know them somewhat, so here goes: First off, notice that it's surprising–really *quite* surprising–that the scientific community hasn't promoted the view that all life is threatened. After all, nothing in this treatise really ought to strike them as novel. They may instinctively be skeptical of the validity of the Vision as a phenomenon, but they certainly ought to have already seen most of my arguments in support of its content.

There are only two obvious factors to which I can attribute their lack of imagination. The first, but least important, is science's devotion to the idea of uniformity. Uniformity, roughly speaking, is the premise that natural changes take place in a continuous manner, usually over rather large periods of time. This proposition is especially strongly advocated whenever the changes are viewed as entailing global phenomena. By this thinking, the overthrow of a phenomenon so well established world-wide as Life would require geologic time scales, unless it were caused via some colossal accident, like the meteor discussed earlier.

Whether this devotion to uniformitarianism is justified is questionable. I especially doubt the wisdom of relying on it in prognostication: there are just too many examples of familiar natural processes that are catastrophic for me to be comfortable with the assumption that large-scale ones might not be similarly triggered.

The second reason is more fundamental and much more insidious. It is a theme worth repeating: western culture is dominated by three religions, Judaism, Islam, and Christianity, all sharing the basic tenet that creation was all about human beings, i.e., that man is at the top of the food chain in every conceivable sense.

In addition, there is some debate in our culture, often quite hot, about whether modern science is itself deserving of the status of a new religion. If so, it is certainly more widely spread than just in the west, but the minds of virtually all of its practitioners are strictly rooted in western thinking. Whether or not science qualifies as a religion, scientists perform much the same function as gurus and high priests. Like religious dogma, their axioms and conclusions are rarely challenged though they pay little or no attention to the "Gödel barrier."[51]

---

[51]Mathematicians are a breed apart, and ought not be considered scientists, for most purposely insulate themselves from reality.

Chemists, physicists, engineers, geologists, etc., being western in orientation, are subconscious devotees of the "its all about us" clan. If science is a religion, it must be the least interested in moral questions of them all. Science seems to regard nothing but humans and their curiosity, as being worthy of consideration. Treating sentient beings as if only human suffering "counts," for example, demonstrates the deepest kind of human-centric bias. For a field that prides itself in its objectivity, one can only explain these kinds of practices by recognizing how deeply ingrained in all of us this bias must lie.

But bias toward humans is *not* objectivity and we shouldn't think it is. It's the kind of chutzpah that got us into this mess in the first place. Scientists don't "get it" for the exact same reason that the Pope doesn't "get it." They buy into the "it's all about us" myth; hook, line, and sinker. Few scientists recognize this predilection, but it's there in every study designed to answer the question, "How will _____ affect humans?" which is how almost every scientific study is couched.

The myth blinds scientists exactly as it does the rest of us. It is the water in which we *all* swim.

Chapter 5
Whence, Then, From Here,
And How Do We Get There?

So, What If It *Isn't* All About Us?

Wait a minute. If I'm so convinced our basic problem is that we can't admit that the universe wasn't specifically created for people, wouldn't finding life on Mars prove that it's really *not* about us and set us off on the right track again?

Well, that's an interesting question.

There's a large set of mostly religious folk for whom such a discovery would have virtually no impact. For them, God is more someone who is always on "our side" than a personification of an idea as abstract as "creator of the universe." That's not everyone of a religious bent, of course, but it's awfully common amongst "fundamentalists"of virtually every sect. "On my side" is just so much more concrete than "creator of the universe."

For many people, however, finding life on Mars would change the whole issue. One of the most common responses to the possibility of there already being life on Mars is, "we sure as hell don't want to mess with it, then." Or, perhaps,"What gives us the right to go destroy someone else's planet?" This is probably the favorite reaction of those most inclined to agree that we are, in fact, killing planet Earth. It's a considerably more valid concern than the irrational fear the we'll simply screw up any planet we terraform just like we did Earth (see "A Reverse Reality Check" in Chapter 3). Here, though, the attitude is more, "Hands off! That planet's already taken," than "We're cursed with the reverse Midas touch."

It should be noted that the current stance of the astronautical community is directly supportive of this "leave other life alone" stance.[52] The trouble with this position is that, despite its popularity, it both totally denies our own tenuous situation on this planet and disregards the most basic characteristic of Life itself: above all, Life is about self-preservation. The "hands off" policy has, *at it's very core*, the assumption that life on this planet is secure, otherwise it defies the survival instinct.

My question: How do we *know* life on this planet is secure? If atmospheres and oceans and ambient temperature on Mars have changed so much that life once indigenous to that planet might now be extinct, then what's the basis of our magnanimity? Aren't we at risk ourselves?

Now, before you freak out more than you already have, let me add that I'm *not* saying that it's perfectly okay to go out there and destroy any other form of Life we might encounter just for the hell of it. *Destroying* is not what I'm talking about. I'm just trying to make two points.

The first is that the assumption that it's "all about us" is *absolutely* everywhere. It's so prevalent that we rarely realize when we are making it. We are especially apt to overlook it when it hides behind any of the hundreds of disguises that "Earth is not *really* threatened" may take. Disguises like the assumption, without evidence, that the water cycle is, and always will be, closed. Or that it *has* to take billions of years for a

---

[52]See, for example, the discussion at http://www.spacedaily.com/news/life-01zg2.html

planet to lose its atmosphere, water, or ambient temperature. The current objection to terraforming Mars is taking yet another disguise: we can afford to leave other worlds alone because *ours* is safe. Why is it safe? Because it is, that's all.

The second point: One of the most basic traits of the Lifeforce is that *every* Lifeform tries to maximize its potential for survival. Whether this takes the form of dominance in mortal combat or of breeding by the millions is irrelevant. What matters is survival, if not of the individual, then of the colony, or the species, or, as in our present situation, the entity that is Gaia. Lifeforms are constantly in battle with one another for available resources. Unfortunately, and unwisely, the extinction of the competitor seems to have become a common outcome where human kind is involved. But we are certainly not unique in having accomplished that, whenever a species has disappeared, a competitor played some role, even if minor, in nudging it out of its niche. Besides, even humans don't generally set elimination of the competition up as the basic goal.

The object, from *any* Lifeform's perspective, is its own survival. And you don't survive by pussy-footing around the needs of the other guy. Life from this planet–Earth life–is *not* secure and *will not be* secure until it is firmly based on at least two planets. That is a fact to which a large number of scientists ascribe, none of whom have ever heard my story of the Vision, let alone support it. *Of course* we ought not go to Mars with the intent of destroying Life there. Obviously, we should do everything in our power to *preserve* any Martian Lifeforms there may be.

But staying off just because some other type of critter might have gotten there first is not an attitude that honors the survival instinct. In fact, it's arrogant and foolish. Arrogant because it assumes we will be as invincible on Mars as we seem to be on Earth and foolish because it ignores changes on our planet that are both evident and ominous. It's the folly of thinking we're safe and sound here on this planet because of our special place at the center of the entire universe. *We're not any of those things.*

As I said in Chapter three, thinking that we will even be capable of screwing up another planet underestimates the difficulty involved in terraforming. It's not simply a matter of time before humans thrive on Mars. I've already discussed a few of the numerous issues which may prevent us truly "getting into" outer space at all. I've also argued that the maximum number of people who may get off this planet in time will be small in any case.

Our supremacy is not the issue. Our survival is.

The first obstacle to a new space policy based on the survival instinct is the deeply seated assumption that all is, and forever will be, well in paradise. Until a sense of urgency exists, there is no chance the public will look past local, parochial matters such as war, poverty and disease to reach for the stars. Therein, of course, lies the irony: if we wait for something on a global scale so drastic that it makes the total failure of the ecosystem obvious to the general public, it will be far too late. When the true problems of Earth's environment are apparent to all, more immediate events, such as rampant genocidal wars, famine, and whole cities dying of thirst, will already be commonplace. Worldwide rivalries will destroy our ability to save ourselves. As suggested earlier, it will be exactly as it was for the victims of the tsunami of 2004–when you can see the tidal wave cresting, it is too late.

Also as discussed earlier, the commonly held view that our activities in space are, and should be, only about exploration is another great obstacle. Until we stop viewing it as merely a means of extending our knowledge base, space will not be so much a frontier as a classroom. That's an insufficient image to inspire a month's worth of dedication, much less multiple centuries'.

Finally, consider this: If life does exist anywhere else in our solar system, it *has* to be struggling. Mars, in particular, is certainly much less hospitable to life in any form today than it has been in its prior history. If there is surviving life there at all, it is just hanging on, barely avoiding ultimate extinction. Life is not presently a growth industry in this stellar system. Should we succeed in terraforming Mars, we will almost certainly create environmental changes that will be welcomed by any extant life remaining there. Earth is the only life-*friendly* planet orbiting Sol. I suspect terraforming will be a wonderful change for any Lifeform still eking out an existence on Mars or anywhere else within our reach. Our impact, if felt at all, is far more apt to be positive, even from the point of view of an alien form. That's pure conjecture, of course, but it seems reasonable to me.

Concerns that Needn't Be

The Vision frees us of some concerns. Some things that make no sense whatsoever if Earth were expected to last forever, no longer need be anathema. For example, why worry about the permanent storage of nuclear waste? Taking nuclear energy off the list of possible tools for fighting global warming because of fears about conditions millennia away is akin to refusing to turn on a hose to fight an early winter house fire because the weatherman thinks there will be a drought next summer. In fact, this example clearly illustrates, once again, the degree to which environmentalists don't believe their own dire predictions: if they truly believed the threat of global warming, would they get so upset about the problems of nuclear waste we may be creating for our great, great, great, great, great, etc., grandchildren? Is the house on fire, or isn't it?

The only truly legitimate problems I see with nuclear power are those of contemporary containment, current environmental impacts, the total mass of waste produced, and security of radioactive materials. They are certainly big enough to be serious, but they seem to me to be much more tractable issues than the one of permanent storage.

Global warming presents a clear and imminent danger. Nuclear waste, insofar as the half-life issues, is only a problem if there really *isn't* any immediate (meaning within the next 5000 years or so) danger of ecological collapse. There *is* clearly such a threat, even if you discount the Vision. We must fear the more pressing, shorter-term problems. What is needed more than a long term storage solution is better technology for making nuclear energy safe *today*.

But, be warned, I claim no real expertise in this issue–it just seems that the popular debate needs to be couched in different terms than I think it has been.

Another, equally important consideration regarding nuclear energy is this: nuclear power will almost certainly be needed if terraforming Mars is to be accomplished in the time frame the Vision implies it must be. The task of freeing or creating water on Mars, alone, will demand huge energy budgets which can only be met with nuclear power. Although creating a dense atmosphere will probably rely largely on terraforganisms, it may also demand a huge expenditure of nuclear power. There is urgency here, folks. We need to get on it. And we need to get on it *hard*.

Long-term problems simply have no appeal to me. I'm far too convinced that the immediate problems are truly critical for me to ixnay potentially useful tools solely because of their having negative, distant down sides. The Message of the Vision was that, on this planet, short-term environmental threats, in the sense of hundreds of years, are the only ones we can any longer hope to solve.

Large Undertakings

The biggest barrier to our getting off this planet is a lack of public support and motivation. A lack of will driven by a lack of vision. While a task so large may seem daunting, we mustn't let the sheer magnitude of the job discourage us. Had we humans contemplated the task of destroying a planet before we set out on doing it, we would have given it up immediately, not just because of its inherent stupidity, but because of the immensity of the project. That one species could jeopardize the entire ecosphere defies comprehension. Yet here we are.

The task of destroying a planet's ecosystem is no less a job than building one. The main difference is intent. The destruction was an unintentional by-product of our vast success at dominating other species. But the magnitude of the job was just as great as what we face today. We had virtually no technology when we set out on the path to destroying the Earth and one might think that speaks encouragingly for our chances as we now start to terraform a planet. Taken in perspective, however, our current technology is not so impressive. In terms of space mechanization, we have barely discovered the equivalent of the wheel. We have the solid fuel rocket and self-contained life support systems; we know about gravity assist; and the solar sail has reached secondary research and development. As far as functioning basic tools go, though, that's about it for now. In particular, our current methods of getting into orbit from the Earth's surface are clearly primitive and represent a major barrier that must be overcome.[53]

It is hard to imagine that the future, if we manage to sustain our place in it long enough, does not hold vast advances in technology which may well cut the several hundreds of years needed to terraform Mars to a mere one or two hundred. This is especially true if we get past our self-imposed restraints on using nuclear power. It's hard to conceive of a much quicker process than this, though, because terraforganisms, even with careful human nurturing, require time to do their magic. But *none* of it will happen unless we are attempting to do it. We will *not* go to outer space automatically. We won't find the task of building a new planet nearly so "serendipitous" as destroying one has been, for it won't be accidental. Space technology is developed by

---

[53]Here is another excellent place for a prize similar to the x-prize. Reward the first developer to successfully lift a payload of $\geq x$ pounds to an altitude of $\geq y$ feet, using a method (system) that convincingly demonstrates an achievable lift cost of $\leq z$ dollars per pound, distributed over the useful life of the system. Again, though, this may already be done. See http://www.spaceward.org/ for a number of such challenges.

traveling into space. Terraforming technology is developed by attempting to terraform a planet–we *must* start the process if we hope to get to Mars in time.

Getting off Earth will not be easy. It will not be quick. We have to rethink the purpose of our Space Program. It must not be random, a mere scientific dalliance. The Space Program needs to focus on one, and only one, goal: establish another planet upon which life can be sustained. Until that's accomplished, life in this part of the galaxy is most definitely insecure. Until then, we are stranded on a sinking ship with no escape.

On Trusting In Magic

At the very start (chapter 1) I told you about Trumpeting. I hope you followed my urging and are now very familiar with it. You'll recall I lost and regained the gift after being without it for fifteen years. While still in the early stages of its recovery, an incident happened which sheds light on how we must proceed if our Movement will have the potential of saving Gaia.

In January of 2004 I had occasion to go to New York City for an extended visit. Being 3000 miles from home, I decided to use the "anonymity of the crowd," to overcome the self-consciousness which I still felt when trying to Trumpet in public. One afternoon I went to the Reservoir in Central Park, a popular jogging place, and there I stood, Trumpeting fairly loudly as hundreds of people ran by. One lady suddenly stopped running and took up a position a few feet from me, obviously to listen. After ten or fifteen minutes, I nodded politely and began to move on. She stopped me by introducing herself and immediately began sharing her story. Her name was Diane and she had developed some kind of lung difficulty from exposure to the toxins that wafted over Manhattan for weeks following the 9-11 attacks. She asked me to put my hands upon her and Trumpet.

Startled, I realized that she wanted me to heal her.

It surprised the Hell out of me. I didn't know what to do. On the one hand, I was totally unprepared to act like a "healer." Yet I certainly didn't want to deny her request, for who am I to question a song taught me by the Lifeforce? Besides, I have a very healthy respect for the placebo effect. Even if the sound itself did not heal her, it could certainly be regarded as an ally in her recovery.

On the other hand, the whole "healer" thing disturbed me mightily. Even as a child, during my devout Southern Baptist phase, I'd always suspected the healing televangelists were just shams. I've steadfastly avoided the trivialization of this book that might come had I presented my message as fiction, but here I was confronting an equally threatening scenario, and one which has worried me from that first day in 1986. Strange things, from my rational, mathematical, conventional perspectives, have propelled me on this task. I fear losing my audience by virtue of the "spirituality" of some of them. As strong as my bond with the sound was, still I had never thought of it as a conduit to miracles–and didn't want to.

I fumbled, I'm afraid. For Diane's sake, I wish I'd had more faith. But I was not prepared to play the part she needed, and I failed her hopeful expectations.

After equivocating a bit, I wound up Trumpeting with my hand placed high over her heart. Twice she asked whether I "felt it," presumably wanting me to confirm its healing nature. Yet I could not respond in the "I'm a channel straight from God pouring strength into your body and soul" way that I know she wanted. I tried to affirm it for her, but I'm sure she could see how taken aback I was by the whole experience. To this day I cannot say how greater faith in Trumpeting might have worked for Diane and I that afternoon. I'm trying to break the shackles rationality has placed firmly upon my expectations of reality. It's a hard task for one as reliant on the scientific approach as I have always been.

When I returned to my friend's Brooklyn apartment, I cried, shaking in a cold sweat for nearly an hour. I was *so* afraid. The episode put an entirely different perspective on my role in this Mission that I am setting out upon. I want only to be a teacher and a leader, not someone's idea of a Messiah. What the hell have I gotten into?

Negative Thinking

As a potential teacher, let me make lessons of the experiences surrounding Trumpeting. The first comes from my having lost it, and it is simply that negative thinking is dangerous and powerful. The loss was prompted by two occasions of embarrassment at how others seemed to interpret my Trumpeting performance. When we expect people to see the world as we do, we risk giving them too much influence. If we depend upon their perception matching our own as confirmation, we are, perhaps, not truly sure of ourselves.

The impact of my friends, Dave and Linda, not being impressed by my Trumpeting that first day, combined with the curious stares of those strangers on the beach, was inhibition. Self-consciousness then completely destroyed my ability to Trumpet.

In New York, I meant Diane no harm–far from it. Yet I'm fairly certain my inability to reflect her perception that I might be a source of tremendous healing power squelched her own hopes for that magic.

And, if anything can create magic, it is hope. The power of positive thinking is arguably far greater than that of negative.

Those of you who recognize and believe in the Vision must not let the doubter's ridicule and incredulousness dissuade you. The Earth will die. All too soon. The only question is whether every species now living on it dies with it or not. And therein lies our power. The power of the knowledge that we can get off this planet. Our Movement is one of hope and promise. We have to get off. And we can. Waver not, for that will only seal our fates. All our fates. Every creature, every plant. Have faith in the truth of the Vision. It is the only hope for any of us—you, or I, or the cockroach. Trust the Magic

Enlightenment

Another lesson from Trumpeting: enlightenment is not permanent. I was enlightened that wonderful day in 1988 on that magical beach. No question. But when I lost Trumpeting, I lost enlightenment. With Trumpeting's return, I've found it again. Yet only during the deepest meditation itself does that sense of peace overwhelm me. Only then can I claim the status of "enlightened."

To be clear, though, enlightenment is not what I am about. Enlightenment is being in a profound state of peace. And it is wonderful. I intend to share that peace at every opportunity.

But I am *about* the Vision. A Vision is a Message and a Command. There is nothing peaceful about living with it. The Lifeforce may have sung to me on that perfect beach, but it shouted orders at me when it dragged me, horrified, through the Vision. The Vision was a whip whose scars I shall always bear.

Enlightenment is a salve. It is love. Love from the Lifeforce Herself.

Staying on Task

There is also a lesson about attaining goals. For all those years without it, I operated on the assumption that, if I could just regain the gift of Trumpeting, everything would be all right. I would be invincible. My message would have infinite appeal. People would flock to hear me talk for the Trumpeting alone. Everyone wants the peace that the sound induced. Needs it, even. With a tool like that, I really *would* be able to "save the world."

So, for years, my most ardent efforts were directed at regaining the Trumpeting. To this day I believe the analysis in the preceding paragraph is correct. The sound is so magical that it cannot be denied. People will come. Bullshit will be shamed into silence.

I understand Trumpeting's role better now than before. It is a tool, not the task. Over the years, the attempt to reclaim the ability became a distraction. It became what I was doing. It was an excuse to avoid talking about having had a Vision. I wasn't warning people about the impending end of the Earth as I had seen it, I was trying to regain a method of deep meditation. I was not facing my Command head-on. I've realized that trying to completely re-master the technique has been a subtle means of avoiding the demands of the Vision.

Trying to recover the ability to Trumpet was a very large part of why I let so many years go to waste. While I will always continue Trumpeting, and will certainly continue to attempt to perfect it's public performance, I have resolved to no longer let the search for my personal enlightenment become an excuse not to pursue the real Mission of my life. I may teach Trumpeting, but it must be learned as a tool. Our focus must never blur. I *will* tell people what was told me. It's time to stop looking at the train and get off the track. *"We're not going to make it. We've got to get off."*

Boundaries

One more lesson from those silent years since 1986: crossing boundaries. One time Barbara and I went to Kuai'i. We spent most of the time snorkeling. You may be aware of one of the frustrations that's inherent in the activity: entering the water can be awkward. If you put your equipment on while still on land, you must walk duck-like (or is that "dork-like") into the ocean. If you wade or swim out past the surf first, though, you find it virtually impossible to get the stuff on.

This is typical of boundaries. They are confusing, difficult, and often dangerous places. One part of you wants to stay in the environment to which you are accustomed. It is safe there. Comfortable, even. You know how it works. You are familiar with the surroundings and there are few surprises. Another part is urging you forward in anticipation of the new experience, eager for the stimulation of the change, knowing, perhaps, that more exhilarating and rewarding surroundings lie just beyond the breakers. But to get there you must first prepare, for some things must be in order *before* you are in the new environment lest it be impossible to accomplish your goals when you arrive. Then, after proper preparation, you must pass through the breakers.

One morning a local came down to where we were about to enter the water. It was in a little cove, so the surf was not great–perhaps two feet or so. Her technique of entry was both simple and astoundingly effective: she donned the snorkel and mask while still on shore but carried her fins with her as she walked out about shin deep. She turned with her back to the waves, sat down, and put them on. Next, instead of standing back up and waddling into the sea, as I surely would have, she simply rolled over onto her stomach in the shallow water and began to swim, letting her arms trail limply from her shoulders as the fins propelled her. She was gone in seconds–and gracefully done! It had never occurred to me that eight to twelve inches of water, on the shore side of the surf, could be enough to swim in.

On thinking about it, I realized this lesson: boundaries are difficult largely because one has to move from commitment to one medium to commitment to another. Some preparation is crucial, for sure, but, in order to make a transition, you have to let go of the familiar first.

The concept of commitment is important in every sport. A very dramatic example is in rock climbing. When changing one's position on a cliff face, leaving the safety of a secure hold to attain a different pose can almost never be done without passing through a point of no return. All then depends upon successfully gaining the new grip. The old must be abandoned in order to reach the new, and, although the transition is meant to be smooth, still the abandonment often must take place before the new grip is assured. There is no way to know, for example, if a granite flake will bear your full weight without placing it there.

The moment when you no longer have the option of going back to the old grip is called "commitment" because, from that instant on, your only hope of staying on the rock is the successful completion of the move: you are committed.

The lesson of the local snorkeler was simply that, in order to cross any boundary, you must commit to the new environment, and the sooner that can be successfully done the better. It took me over 16 years to decide to commit to the Vision. I only hope I do not waver, for therein lies a foolproof formula for failing.

This lesson applies to every new venture. The bigger the venture, the truer the lesson. *If you hear my call, commit to it.* Give up clinging to hope that Life on Earth will be eternal and join in the project of preserving Gaia long after Earth has died. Give up on the insane idea that the universe was created especially for us and that we are entitled to trash everything around us if it suits our whim. Become a participant in the Lifeforce itself, not just the human version. And don't dawdle at the boundary. Commit to preserving the Lifeforce *today*. No, do it **now**!

Non-Violence

I promised earlier to speak to the role of non-violence in our Movement. During the Reagan years, Common Sense sponsored many excursions by Tahoe locals to peace demonstrations at the Nuclear Test Site (NTS) in Nevada, where the United States conducts all of its nuclear weapons tests. There, I took numerous training sessions in the techniques of non-violent civil disobedience and was arrested several times for trespassing as we (the protesters) tried to apply pressure to stop all nuclear testing. Prior to those experiences I had long been interested in non-violent resistance as exemplified by the movements of Martin Luther King Jr., the Buddhist monks in Vietnam, and Mahatma Gandhi.

During the Vietnam war, some of the most powerful and enduring images were photos of

Vietnamese Buddhist monks setting themselves on fire in protest of the American presence and the puppet government we had in place there. Such images did much to undermine American support of the war and were instrumental in America's eventual withdrawal.

The Israeli-Palestinian conflict confirms the lesson via contrast: non-violence is a far more effective technique than violence. Violence is most powerful when used by the stronger of two adversaries. Governments and armies can reliably dominate people and/or weaker armies by literally killing, torturing, and terrorizing them. The weaker and less well organized groups wishing to effect change cannot. The occasional cataclysms of outright rebellion, which almost invariably spiral out of everyone's control, are the exceptions that prove the rule: the only truly successful tools available to the masses, or to causes greatly mismatched against ingrained powers, are non-violent ones.

The Palestinians would have won their struggle, or at least have reached a reasonable solution to their many problems with Israel, years ago had they never adopted the technique of suicide bombings, but instead chosen to self-immolate. At my last count, about 2000 people have killed themselves in attempts to murder Israelis. Certainly fewer than 200 Buddhist monks made the same sacrifice during Vietnam. It was probably even closer to twenty. Yet their impact was quite effective in galvanizing resistance amongst American youth to the War. Two thousand suicides for a cause, minus the even larger number of murders that went with them, would have been an absolutely irresistible force on the side of the Palestinians. Calmly sitting down and lighting themselves on fire would have been infinitely more effective at gaining what these "martyrs" wanted. Without the murders, the question, "why are there so many people willing to kill themselves rather than to tolerate the situation?" would have lifted Palestinian grievances as a tide lifts boats. They'd have won over world opinion and long since reached reasonable accommodation with Israel.

But the murders allow the more powerful Israelis to avoid the spotlight entirely. Assisted by the one-sided reporting in the Western hemisphere, every suicide assault becomes another nail in the coffin of the Palestinian cause–such is the danger of violent resistance, especially when practiced by a people totally outmatched by a dominant hostile government.

Judo

In college I was on the judo team. There I learned another valuable lesson: an opponent's weight and momentum can be either overwhelming or his downfall. Given equal skills, the bigger judoka will win almost every time. In every fight the advantage of weight can only be overcome by either a much greater advantage in either speed or strength, a much more modest advantage in skill, or a combination of these. It should be noted, too, that the heavier contestant is almost always the stronger, and luck is virtually never a factor, so it usually falls to speed and skill to overcome the weight advantage.

A skilled judoka urges his opponent to commit his momentum to a direction–almost any direction will do–and then uses that momentum against him to throw him to the ground, winning the contest. Since weight tends to manifest itself as momentum, the more skilled contestant can morph his opponent's strongest feature into a weakness. The same is true of virtually every type of contest.

In every conflict between ideas, the established idea is the heavyweight. The favorite tools of the heavyweight are ridicule and violence: ridicule if the opponent is perceived as weak, violence if the threat is seen as real. Violence is, in every case, a commitment of momentum. We must not be deterred by ridicule and be ever vigilant to utilize the momentum that the establishment's exercise of violence provides us, when it comes, to win the sympathy of the masses.

The art of enticing the opponent into an ill-considered commitment of momentum is much more like a dance than a fight. It is more marshaling of forces than use of force. A tug here, a push there. Provocations, prods, pressure first on the left, then the right, then a big pull to urge the opponent off balance. The situation in terms of the struggle we will face is similar. Our task is to manipulate the momentum of the establishment. If we resort to violence we fall into a trap: a premature attempt to apply a throw by a judoka will always throw him/her off balance and leave him/her very vulnerable to counterattack, often leading to defeat.

We are not in a position where we have the luxury of trusting in the fumbling of our opponents. Luck must not figure in our calculations. This fight will, very likely, have to be won in the first round, as there may not be time left for recoveries from missteps.

I have never been a pacifist. Nor am I now. But I have always thought of myself as a strategic thinker, and it is crucial to The Movement that we *all* understand that violence at this stage, and for the stages through many coming generations, at least, is absolutely against our best interests. It must be totally absent from of our practice. I frankly cannot imagine there every being a time when violence will help our cause, for, as with true judoka masters, I expect the final triumph of our

Movement to be nothing more than assisting the old thinking to complete its fall. But, in any case, that will not occur for some considerable time. Time which will only be extended if someone in The Movement brings disrepute to it by letting anger at some provocation lead to a public perception that we have caused death or injury, or probably even destruction of property. "Turn the other cheek," is Christ's greatest, most powerful, legacy. Let us adopt it.

Maintaining the Balance

A final judo note: maintaining one's own balance despite the opponent's maneuvers is also critical in any contest. I'm afraid my presentation thus far may have thrown you off balance. It is not my intent to send you to the same place I was for so long following seeing the Vision: that place of utter depression. I have wanted you to taste of it, for without a taste I fear you will continue on that path toward utter destruction of the Lifeforce you, and all the rest of us, are currently on. But there's a definite danger to your drinking too deeply from that well. I was immobilized for eighteen years. We can't have that happen to everyone who first begins to "see the dark," as it were. It's a luxury we cannot afford.

You may not be so greatly handicapped by despair as I was. You've had the gentle version of the Vision. You've been able to put this book down whenever it seemed too depressing, or overwhelming, or crazy, or whatever. It's come to you in the time it's taken you to read it. It wasn't the instant shock that looking up and staring the death of Gaia in the face was for me. You've had time to build up defenses to the Message as it has been delivered. So, hopefully, you are not as likely to be overwhelmed and immobilized as I was.

However, if I've succeeded in convincing you of the inevitability of the death of Paradise, I cannot imagine that you are anywhere but in despair. If that is the case, I suggest you adopt the technique I'm using myself to overcome the depression that thinking about these things invites. The task that is set me (and you) is *not* about death. In particular, it is not about the death of this planet. The death of Earth is a floodlight illuminating the task. I–we–must not look directly at it, or we will be blinded by it. Our task is about Life and about preserving and propagating it.

When I look out over a landscape, I have a choice. Seeing the death of all the amazing life that makes it so beautiful is one option I, especially, have. For so I saw it once. But also it is possible to see–to really *appreciate*–the astounding abundance of life such settings always present exactly as they are: alive and vibrant. Stunningly exciting in their vigor and full of promise and hope. And this is what the present reality is. It is what is *now*. The ancient wisdom of "be here now" is irrefutable. This is Paradise now. We are blessed beyond comprehension. And we are thus blessed *right now*. Life is such an incredible miracle. Revel in it. Living in the present will give us strength unimaginable. Celebrate Life! For it is truly joyous.

One final thought on depressing topics: earlier I waxed pessimistic about the future for those beings that do reach Mars because of how hard the environment there will be. Since then, I've realized how rampant that speculation was. I know nothing about how good or bad conditions on Mars will be 300-900 years from now. By then, terraforganisms may have made Mars into the next Garden of Eden and it may, indeed, be a Promised Land. In fact, in that time frame it will most likely be much the better of the two worlds. Human Martian populations will be tiny. I think that not very speculative at all. So, for Gaia's survivors, Mars may be a new world on the model of Earth's ancient history: a new Paradise.

But that is not *now*. Now *we* have Paradise. We can–should–and, really, must–rejoice in Her. And we must do that *now*.

What's A Life Good For, Anyway?

Every person's life is like a golden statuette that we carve by living it. It has immense innate value, but its true worth is in the craftsmanship of its artistry. Each of us has different tools with which to carve it–wealth, intelligence, the capacity to love, the love that is shared with us–all of our strengths and weaknesses, all of our good, and bad, luck, everything that happens during our time here in Gaia's body.

Love is the most powerful of the tools, and produces the best results.

Like the ripples in the surf that eventually disappear by becoming indistinguishable in the tide of ebb and flow that the ocean is, each of us is a little glom of energy that eventually dissipates after our deaths into the surge of vitality that is everything, everywhere.

The work of art that we were while alive is melted down and inevitably disappears. Yet it has a lingering effect in the way it shapes the lives of others that knew it. If the work was particularly good, other artists will attempt to imitate it, hence we remember such great people as Christ, Mohammed, Buddha, Confucius, Gandhi, Lao-Tse, Martin Luther King Jr., etc long after they have died. Yet we all make ripples and our only certain immortality lies in these expanding circles of our energy.

Directions

Forgive me it I'm sounding too presumptuous here. The fact of the matter is that I suspect those who are still reading this now, so late in the text, are with me. I've never been one who thinks that talking is as effective as acting. So I intend to start something here. And I'm counting on you to follow my lead.

As the first recipient of the Vision to acknowledge it, as my mother's son, and as who I am, I cannot help but adopt working on the Vision as my project from now until my death. I have a duty. As do you, if you see it too.

Let me share some of my thinking of how the task may be accomplished. First, what is clearly essential is that we start a movement. This book is my first step in that direction. Knowing what I do of people's tendencies to let day to day activities occlude longer range and more abstract goals, however, I am loath to let that simple claim be the end of it. Not even the series of books I intend to write on this subject will do the trick. This is not a spectator sport, and reading is a barely disguised version of voyeurism. We need an active movement–something which will guide people through their daily lives.

Determination such as Pann showed that day when he and I were getting thirsty and we were far from water is exactly what we will need as a species if we are to get out of the situation we find ourselves in today. It won't be only up to those of us who decide to band together now. We will need to impassion our fellow humankind with an awareness that will motivate them all to join us in the endeavor. That, in itself, will take tremendous time and effort. Ours must grow to be a mass movement. We'll need the resolve of these masses for possibly centuries, so we must find ways to pass the passion down and sustain it through generations.

This is a work that will demand large investments of time, energy and money from a great many individuals. We must be a unit. Certainly, though, this is only the first step on a long, long journey. My (our) early expectations are of work on the person to person level. We are laying a foundation. Great things absolutely *must* come of this. But for now it's talks at service club meetings and gatherings in people's homes and at the local library. It's web sites, blogs, and text messages. For now it's one to one or at best one to a few. For now it is collecting a core group of dedicated individuals and organizing an infrastructure. It's Trumpeting for meditation. It's talking with friends and acquaintances. It's giving this book to someone you care for.

On The Role Of Money
One lesson I learned from that side trip I went on shortly after the Vision, Common Sense–you remember, the environmental/peace group that diverted my attention for a while–was about money. The group's focus attracted people who weren't interested in hearing my Message that efforts to save the planet are destined to fail, and I told no one, except a very few trusted friends and my wife. I was just entering my sixteen year long period of trying to logically refute the Message.

Common Sense was mostly an energetic form of avoidance. But it did teach me some very important lessons which will come in handy now that I'm no longer in that mode. One was that the success of any significant venture depends very directly upon whether or not it generates money.

Despite having a great deal of appeal and some wonderful ideas and activities, despite an excellent newsletter and a growing following, Common Sense languished and died because I, as its figurative and actual leader, never embraced fund-raising. We never had more than $500 in our accounts at a time and were never in a position to hire a staff, or even incorporate. Gradually the dedicated core or volunteers burned out and began to withdraw. No one could be found to take their place. Eventually it fell to me, virtually alone, to keep the group going. After some five or six years as president, I resigned. No one stepped up to take the reins. Common Sense slipped into quiescence and remained there until this year (2006), when I decided to use it as the base for launching the new organization which we're discussing here.

Fund-raising is a task many environmentally inclined people find distasteful. To me, it almost smacks of begging. There are, of course, many ways to raise funds which do not involve direct solicitation of donations. The reality of modern organizational politics, however, is that direct solicitation is a necessity.

Any "movement" we undertake must embrace this activity. The task we are undertaking is too important to let squeamishness hinder our efforts. Never hesitate to ask for financial support. The task is too important to go unstructured or underfunded.

On Structure

The structure must remain flexible within some definite restraints, as there must be plenty of room to grow and yet we cannot lose sight of where we must go with this: the goal is terraforming Mars. Yet, to last centuries, it must have practical guidance for our daily lives.

If it is to provide guidance for how to live, there must be axioms, but only a few. Inviting contradictions is truly worse than acknowledging our inability to answer most of life's "interesting" questions. Yet those few axioms must strike at the heart, for no work can be passed to future generations unless it be passed at the gut level. If our children are to pick up the burden, it must be a labor of love and hope.

Love of the Lifeforce is the easiest thing in the world to instill. But only if the young are exposed to Her. In generations past this was unavoidable, for She flourished virtually everywhere. But today most children rarely get to go where man is not, which is the only place She continues to thrive today. Now, and in the future, exposure to nature will only happen to the extent that we make it happen. Our children (the children of The Movement) must not be allowed to grow up without regular, frequent, and prolonged periods in the wild. We must actively pursue every opportunity to raise children aware of nature.

Our greatest challenge, however, will be to provide hope for generations bred and raised in the deteriorating flesh of the fallen fruit of knowledge that modern culture has become. We have deprived our progeny of hope. We've done this by talking about the environment in terms of "fire and brimstone" while simultaneously doing nothing to reverse our steady march into the caldron. Our children believe us when we predict the end of the world at our own doing. They see it happening all around them. More than the older generations, they recognize that our only hope of survival following a worldwide ecological collapse is to go to outer space. The Movement will give them a place to direct their hope.

The task of keeping the axioms few and simple is daunting. I will attempt my part by citing only two and urging us all to never adopt more than five. The first is, I think, a better formulation of the version I gave in Chapter 4.

> 1) Love the Lifeforce more than anything, including your own species, and including your own self.

and 2) The planet Earth will not be saved as a home of the Lifeforce.

I think " we've got to get off," with the large meaning of "we," is then an obvious first theorem. So, too, are the propositions that 1) We must recognize that humans do not play a more precious role in the universe than does any other species, and 2) We must do everything possible to prevent further environmental decline here on Earth. Then my stated goal regarding abstaining from greed will follow (Chapter 4, "First Principles").

Beyond these comments, and premises, the infrastructure of the Movement must, I think, be developed over time and that will be the first part of our work.

Beziers Revisited

The train is bearing down on us, rocking violently side to side. An ice shelf falls into the sea in Antarctica, an asteroid misses the Earth by the astronomical equivalent of inches, the ozone layer develops a huge hole. Vast regions of the ocean go lifeless. We learn that Mars lost its water, atmosphere, and heat. America decides to militarize space and other nations follow. The globe begins to noticeably warm. Amphibians mysteriously disappear from ecosystems the world over. China becomes a first-world industrial nation, complete with consumerism typical of first-world nations. Mass extinctions become routine, genocidal wars amongst humans all too common. Look at it only long enough to recognize that we are doomed if we don't get off this planet. And, please remember that "we" here is a reference to all Gaians *not* just people. Don't look at the train for too long, though. Get off the track!

If you are not convinced, put this book down and begin, instead, to appraise our situation for yourself. Go ahead, look at the train. Some preparation is definitely needed before you can commit to an environment as new and alien as this one: the one in which Earth's future is that of a broken shell. But *do* look. Stop ignoring those dreary stories on the news, in the papers, on the internet, or at the dinner party about the demise of the environment. Tune out of the sports channel and the game shows–we don't have time for you to continue wasting your life. Do some actual research into global warming and the depletion of the ozone layer and the decline of the oceans and *don't* trust politicians on this. Politicians are too often prostitutes to the rich, and those masters will be among the last people to come around, for the monied classes have tremendous momentum and will be the hardest to turn.

Don't be fooled, either, by the optimistic caveats of every other environmental book you've ever read: their hope for saving Earth is not rational–their own arguments prove it–it is only wishful thinking. Think beyond the protestations and remonstrations about what "needs to be done" to the consequences of *not* doing those things. Realize that almost none of the things that need to be done are, in fact, *being* done; or at least admit that *most* of the things that need to be done on a worldwide scale aren't. Begin to recognize the magnitude of the problem. The environment is not some abstraction, and it is *not about* us humans. When you realize the truth of the Vision, come back.

If, on the other hand, you see the obvious–for it *is* obvious–then talk about it. *Be* the one at the dinner party who has the bad taste to point out that time is rapidly running out. *Be* the one who devotes his schooling to the study of arcane and difficult subjects with the sole purpose of contributing some small molehill to the mountain that getting off this planet will be. Do without. Wash and reuse a plastic bag. Vote against an "industry rep." *Be* the little guy who contributes to the most important element of all in this project–public support; *active* public support for the only realistic solution there is: building the lifeboat.

The only strength is in numbers, and, as I mentioned earlier, money. First must come the numbers. Public support is absolutely critical. Lack of it is the only reason we do not already have manned space stations on Mars, let alone the Moon, these four decades after Apollo. But be aware that public support must be for something more specific than just some vague idea of going to the stars, and more important than idle curiosity. Insist on a space program not of scientific exploration, but of development and human occupation (remember–only a goal of human occupation will succeed for *any* species).

There is no time for playing at it. We must get off this planet. We need a viable place to survive other than just Earth!

If you have money (and we all have *some*), throw it at us. It's never too soon for that. Gather together, for it never rains a single drop, and we need a flood.[54] At the least, join your voice with ours: become a member.

Above all else, what we need is for the public to realize the stupidity of our not recognizing the danger Gaia Herself is in, and of our necessary role in the only appropriate response. Humans can get us off this planet. *People* may even be included in that exodus. But only if we decide we need to; only if there is a public outcry for it; and only if we start *soon*. Given the will, the science will follow. The money will follow. The technology will follow. You can–you must–help build the will.

A New Eco-Religion

There are two kinds of intellectual power: passion and logic. Given time, reason will eventually overcome passion. But no amount of reason can overrule passion in the short term, for true passion gains strength in the face of being thwarted.

Our goal will take generations to be reached, and the task of passing on to following generations those values which are most important cannot be treated like a fad. "The movement" is how we thought of our revolution in the Sixties. But although it was, indeed, a revolution, that it largely failed to reach its full potential seems evident. A "movement," in the sense that the sixties was a "movement," will not do.

The greatest challenge facing us is that of inflaming, and then maintaining, the passion. Reason is already on our side, for the evidence irresistibly leads to the same, inevitable conclusion I was shown in the flash

---

[54] Go to http://www.intheserviceofgaia.com to join, donate, and/or subscribe to our newsletter.

of an instant in 1986. But this reason will have to be cultivated, and merely being convinced is insufficient. We must arouse people's passion. If you've already realized the tenuous nature of Life's existence on this planet, and recognize the truth of the Vision, then **you** must act. Tell others of the imminent tragedy of the death of Gaia and recruit those who have noticed that Earth is in decline but who remain in denial. Thus far I've attempted to appeal to your reason. But I'm done with that now. Passion is the final ingredient you need.

Passion is the essence of religion. Religion *is* passion. Religion is the essence of a Vision. It was a Vision which started me on this most extraordinary path I now tread–that I will tread until my works begin to disperse upon the vastness of this ocean of Life that surrounds us all. From that Vision comes *my* passion. Some of you may already share that passion by virtue of having seen the same Vision as I. Others will have to light their own fire from within–or from the heat of the passion of those who have it.

However it comes, we must have the fire.

Two years after the Vision, I was given a magical sacrament, Trumpeting. Through Trumpeting I envision a means of nurturing passion, both mine and yours. So teaching and practicing this art will be a central part of my efforts to spread and nurture passion.

If my words have struck a common chord with you, join me in this undertaking in whatever ways you can.

But we need a word other than "religion" to describe our Movement. "Religion" bears with it the onus of centuries of human-centric manipulation of power. So, to the end of achieving the goal of preserving Life in this portion of the universe; to the end of acknowledging that this is a passionate endeavor which must not–*cannot*–fail; to the end of honoring the mystery of the Vision, and of Life itself; to the end of fulfilling the Mission; to the end of teaching our children the true value of Life: I call upon you to join me in forming a new kind of Movement; One based in passion for Gaia, not a religion in the old sense, but even more precious and central to our lives–an eco-religion–for lack of a better term.

On many levels it will be a meld of the world's greatest old religions, for much of the morality preached and practiced for centuries is essential to leading a good life, and our faith must pay homage to both their spirit and much of their letter. Developing all the nuances of our practice is not a work for one of us alone. Our Movement must blend East and West. It will be developed over time, possibly years, by our earliest devotees, and will be the subject of volume two in this series.

But, on one most basic level, our Movement is, and will always remain, an utter rejection of most, if not all, historical religions. Mankind is not, and never has been, the central player in the universe. Our task is not to get mankind off of this planet–although, I repeat, that would be absolutely lovely, and we must adopt it as a subgoal to appeal to the unenlightened. But our task has nothing to do with the supremacy of humans over animals or even plants–just the opposite. To us, all Gaians are precious beyond belief, and no species, including Homo sapiens, is more important than any other. Our eco-religion has nothing to do with humans being somehow special. That's a model of the universe that harbors tragedy beyond belief. Our only task in the grand scheme of things is simply to preserve Earth-originated life.

The Lifeforce itself is our God. The universe is not about us, it is about Life–and we are about the Earth based version, Gaia. Our prayers are to Life as we know it, to Gaia. Trumpeting is the meditative form our prayers take. Our devotion is to preserving Life–the wonder of it, the joy of it, the mystery of it, the uniqueness of it. To honoring it in all of its forms. Not the life of any individual, for individuals are only transitional manifestations of Life. Life is our God. Not you, nor me, nor the cow I will not eat, nor the grain of wheat I will. Life is *so* much bigger and better than its representatives. Life as God so much more clearly explains the phrase "Man was made in God's image." *Every* living creature is made in God's image. Life is God. And we must save it. For it is surely threatened, and we are both its greatest threat and the only hope it has. We will save it by turning a tragic ending into a new start. It is our only option, so we do not so much end this treatise as set out on the next phase. Hence:

–The Beginning–

Acknowledgments

The people who've made this work possible are far too numerous to list exhaustively, so I regret I can only acknowledge those who have been most important, and pray I haven't overlooked any of those:

Barbara: 23 years of love and support, not the least of which came in the form of repeated edits of the manuscript when it was in its rawest forms, and incredible tolerance of a pretty intolerable personality.

Pann: 30 or so years of friendship, support and encouragement. Countless hours and unequaled computer expertise without which none of this would have had a chance.

Lee: Recent friendship and wonderful tolerance and support as I ventured through the east, imposing liberally on her hospitality.

Linda and Rick: Long standing friendship and especially 6 weeks of helping Barb and I over the hump the last push proved to be.

Jim: 30 or so years of friendship, support and encouragement. Talent as a photographic artist like no one I know.

Steve: Long standing friendship, a shared belief in the urgency of protecting Gaia, Wednesday morning coffees and financial support without which reviving CS wouldn't have happened. But especially for showing me the transcendent power of performance.

Kris and Roger: Unwavering friendship and love lasting at least 16 years and never faltering faith in me as a person. You keep me in touch with who I was before the Vision, and who I must, somehow, remain despite it.

Mike and Rika: Long standing friendship, support, and earliest examples of people whose insight into the world were so much broader than mine that I began to question my own, narrow, version of reality.

Elfriede: Long standing friendship, editing feedback, honesty non-parallel, and the repeated lending of the binding machine.

Rod and Pat: Almost 40 years of friendship, albeit interrupted, support and excellent editing (Pat).

Dan: Probably the first to clearly understand me and the giver of perhaps the best editing advice I've gotten. Originator of the phrase "Dead Planet Spinning."

Liz: Long standing friendship, great editing under unreasonable time restraints, and common values.

Chelsea: Longstanding friendship and gifted artist whose eye catching work promises to do more for Gaia than any 1000 of my words.

Mike: Another recent friend, helpful New York City host and the first to do official pro bono work for CS3rd.

E.J.: New-found friend and great recording resource—the father of the newest version of the Trumpeting C.D.

Max and Janiene: Earliest readers of a manuscript so different they won't recognize this as having been derived from it, but their encouragement was critical.

All those under 30 who attended the going away party July 26, 2006: For showing me who my audience is: the young and very intelligent. The future of the world quite literally is in your hands.

All those many others who helped along the way and I should have mentioned, but didn't: It's why I hate making lists.